Methuen's Monographs on Physical S...

General Editor: B. L. WORSNOP, F...

P

MOLECULAR BEAMS

METHUEN'S MONOGRAPHS ON PHYSICAL SUBJECTS

General Editor : B. L. WORSNOP, B.Sc., Ph.D.

F'cap 8vo, 2s. 6d. net (except where otherwise stated)

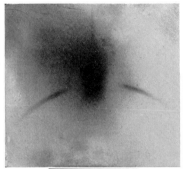

FIG. 6.—Diffraction of Hydrogen Atoms by Li F — 110 Incidence (Johnson)

FIG. 13. — Magnetic Deflection Pattern, Lithium (Taylor)

FIG. 19.—Electric Deflection Pattern, Pentaerythritol (Estermann)

MOLECULAR BEAMS

by

R. G. J. FRASER, Ph.D.

Imperial Chemical Industries Limited

WITH A FRONTISPIECE AND 22 DIAGRAMS

METHUEN & CO. LTD.

36 ESSEX STREET W.C.

London

First published in 1937

PRINTED IN GREAT BRITAIN

FOR

L. F. B., J. H. L., T. N. J., A. G. E., J. V. H., R. S.,
S. A. M. AND J. L. P. :

UNIDIRECTIONAL AND COLLISION-FREE

PREFACE

OF the two ways in which it seemed to me possible to write a short monograph of some fifteen thousand words—either to give a telegraphic account of everything which had been done in the field of molecular beams, or to describe in something like adequate detail its more fruitful areas only—I have followed the second. Although inevitably personal judgement, or even predilection must influence such a selective description, I cannot feel that anything at least of present importance has been left out.

My thanks are due to Dr. H. S. W. Massey, who read and criticized the initial draft of Chapter II; to Professor I. I. Rabi, who gave me many details of work in progress in a valued correspondence, and who has read the section on Nuclear Spins and Magnetic Moments; and to Professor O. Stern and Professor I. Estermann for communicating to me the results of their more recent experiments on the nuclear moments of the proton and the deuteron. Dr. G. B. B. M. Sutherland has read the complete text, to the notable diminution of its obscurity.

R. G. J. F.

CAMBRIDGE
October 1936

CONTENTS

CHAPTER I

MOLECULAR BEAMS

THE study of corpuscular beams—directed, collision-free streams of discrete particles—has almost invariably given the most direct and immediate information about the properties of the individual constituents. Beams of charged particles, electrons and ions, were, however, investigated for two decades before the first beams of neutral molecules, moving with thermal velocities, were produced in the laboratory by Dunoyer in 1911. The delay was largely an accident of technique, for the production of collision-free beams of neutral molecules, of a length great enough to make their examination feasible, had to await the introduction of the fast pumps, having a high end vacuum, which followed the demands of the lamp and valve industries.

The apparatus used by Dunoyer [*] in his pioneer experiments was a quite primitive arrangement; but it held all that is even now essential to the production of molecular beams, and illustrates perfectly the characteristic features of the method. Dunoyer divided an evacuated glass tube, some 20 cm. long, into three compartments by means of two circular diaphragms. He introduced a little redistilled sodium into the first chamber, then heated it until it began to vaporize. After some minutes, a deposit of metallic sodium appeared on the closed end of the third compartment, having precisely the form and dimensions ('umbra' and 'penumbra') to be expected, on the

* Dunoyer, *Compt. rend.*, **152**, 594, 1911; *Le Radium*, **8**, 142, 1911.

assumption that the sodium atoms described straight-line paths between source chamber and deposit (fig. 1).

The selective action of the diaphragms bounding the collimator chamber had translated the chaotic motion of the molecules in the source chamber into a co-ordinated motion in the observation chamber. Here the molecules move in a geometrically defined ray or beam, which, although obviously divergent, may be regarded with good

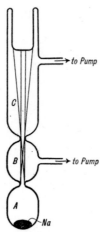

FIG. 1.—Illustrating Dunoyer's Apparatus

A—Source Chamber
B—Collimator Chamber
C—Observation Chamber

approximation as *unidirectional*, if the beam is made sufficiently narrow.

The molecules in the beam move with the thermal velocities determined by their mass and by the temperature of the source. It follows that they are not all moving with the same velocity: rather, that their velocities are grouped about a most probable value reflecting the Maxwell distribution which governed them in the source chamber. Thus there will be a certain number of intermolecular collisions in the beam, due to the faster molecules overtaking the slower ones ; nevertheless the effect is small, and for all practical purposes a molecular beam may be considered *collision free*.

These salient features of molecular beams, their unidirectional and collision-free character, may be illustrated by two especially apt examples.

Hyperfine Structure (H.F.S.) of Spectral Lines. The resolution of the H.F.S. of spectral lines is limited, not by the resolving power of modern spectroscopic apparatus, but by the Doppler effect arising from the thermal motion of the radiating atoms towards or away from the observer. Several ways of overcoming this difficulty have been devised, among them one which takes advantage of the unidirectional character of molecular beams. Thus if the molecules of a beam are excited to emit radiation, and the now luminous beam is viewed at right angles to its direction, the Doppler broadening of the spectral lines is very greatly reduced. As a concrete example, we may take the case of a beam of lithium atoms, angular aperture 10^{-4}, the atoms in which are moving with velocities corresponding to a temperature of some $10^{3°}$ K, which has been made luminous by irradiating it with the light of its own resonance lines : when viewed at right angles the Doppler broadening of the lines emitted from the beam corresponds to a temperature of only some $10°$ K.

In this way the H.F.S. of the lithium $\lambda 6708$ line,[*] the sodium D-lines,[†] and (in absorption) the potassium resonance lines[‡] $\lambda 7699$ and $\lambda 7665$ have been examined. A molecular beam may also be made luminous by a high-frequency discharge, using a carrier gas,[§] or by electron bombardment,[‖] and the latter method has been used to examine the red cadmium line, $\lambda 6438$.

[*] Bogros, *Compt. rend.*, **190**, 1185, 1930 ; *Ann. d. Phys.*, **17**, 149, 1932.

[†] Dobrezov and Terenin, *Naturwiss.*, **33**, 656, 1928.

[‡] Jackson and Kuhn, *Nature*, **134**, 25, 1934 ; *Proc. Roy. Soc.*, **A, 148**, 335, 1935.

[§] Bogros and Esclangon, *Compt. rend.*, **195**, 368, 1932.

[‖] Minkowski and Bruck, *Z. Physik*, **95**, 274 ; 284, 1935.

Free Radicals. Fraser * has drawn attention to the possibilities of the molecular beam method in the study of free radicals, such as CH_3 and C_2H_5 ; for the collision-free character of molecular beams allows such fleeting products of chemical reactions to be examined at a distance of some tens of centimetres from their place of birth. Recently it has been found possible to make beams of free methyl and free ethyl, to detect them with a refined ionization gauge, and to measure their ionization potentials.† There are interesting possibilities here for future experiments ; for example, a determination of the dipole moment of free methyl would give valuable information about its spatial structure (see p. 64).

MOLECULAR BEAM TECHNIQUE

The full realization of the distinctive features of the molecular beam method is due to Stern. One wishes, for example, to study the mechanism of intermolecular collisions—the spreading of a molecular beam as it traverses a gas-filled region is measured ; one looks for information about the magnetic or electric properties of molecules —the deviation suffered by a beam shot through a magnetic or electric field is observed. These are experiments which are primitive in conception ; but, as will appear later, the developed technique is subtle, and the results got with it have often asked much in patience and experimental skill. The development of the technique as a definite method in research was achieved, in all its essentials, by Stern and numerous collaborators in the Institute for Physical Chemistry in Hamburg in the years between 1923 and 1933. This technical development was in a great measure incidental to the accomplishment of a notable series of some thirty investigations, the most important of which will be discussed, each in its proper place, in subsequent chapters. Here we shall outline very briefly the main features of the technique.

Molecular Streaming. A molecular beam must be dis-

* Fraser, *Trans. Faraday Soc.*, **30**, 182, 1934.
† Fraser and Jewitt, *Proc. Roy. Soc.*, 1937.

tinguished from a jet of vapour, such as the steam jets issuing from the nozzles of a steam turbine : a molecular beam is, as we have seen, practically collision free ; within a jet, on the other hand, there is streamlined or turbulent motion of the vapour in bulk. Whether the vapour issuing from the source is to be a molecular stream or a jet depends on the *pressure conditions* in the source ; more precisely, on the relation between the mean free path λ and the dimensions d of the orifice—in the case of a slit-shaped orifice, the *width* of the slit. If $\lambda \gg d$, there is molecular streaming through the orifice ; if $\lambda \ll d$, hydrodynamic flow. There is thus no sharp criterion for molecular streaming ; it passes gradually over into hydrodynamic flow as the pressure in the source is increased. For practical purposes, however, we may lay down the condition for molecular streaming as : $\lambda \lessgtr d$.*

Beam Intensities. This condition sets an upper limit to the *intensity* of molecular beams : where by intensity is meant the number of molecules passing through unit area of cross-section of the beam per second. The beam intensity is readily calculated, for there is an exact analogy between the laws of molecular streaming and of radiation ; both follow a cosine law,† and the intensity at a distance r from the source, in a direction making an angle θ with the normal to the source orifice, is consequently

$$I_\theta = \tfrac{1}{4}.n\bar{c}.a.\cos\theta/\pi r^2 \quad . \quad . \quad . \quad (1.1)$$

where n is the number of molecules per cm.^{3} in the source, $\bar{c}$ their mean velocity, and a the area of the source orifice. Now the angular aperture of the beams used in practice is so small that we may take θ to be zero, and

$$I = \frac{\nu.a}{\pi r^2} \quad . \quad . \quad . \quad . \quad (1.2)$$

* Knauer and Stern, *Z. Physik*, **39**, 774, 1926 ; Kratzenstein, ibid., **93**, 279, 1935 ; also Fraser, *Molecular Rays*, Cambridge, 1931, p. 17 ff.
† Knudsen, *Ann. Physik*, **28**, 999, 1909 ; cf. also Mayer *Z. Physik*, **52**, 235, 1928.

where $v = \frac{1}{4}n\bar{c}$. In terms of temperature and pressure, we have finally

$$I = \frac{N_0}{\sqrt{2\pi RMT}}.\frac{pa}{\pi r^2} \text{ molecules/cm.}^2\text{sec.} \quad . \quad (1.3)$$

where N_0 is Avogadro's number, R the gas constant per mole, and M the molecular weight of the gas; p being, of course, expressed in dynes/cm.^{2}.

An idea of the actual magnitude of the obtainable intensity is best got from a specific example. Let us consider a source containing mercury vapour at 100° C., at which its vapour pressure is of the order 3×10^{-1} mm. Remembering the useful rule of thumb that the mean free path is around 10^{-1} mm. at a pressure of 10^{-1} mm., we find as an approximate upper limit to the width of a slit aperture, $d = 3 \times 10^{-2}$ mm.; let us set its length arbitrarily at 5 mm. Inserting these values in equation (1.3), we have for the intensity of our mercury beam at a distance of 10 cm. from the source

$$I = 2 \times 10^{14} \text{ atoms/cm.}^2\text{sec.}$$

This corresponds to the rate at which atoms arrive at the boundary walls of a vessel containing mercury vapour at room temperature and a pressure of only some 10^{-6} mm.

A molecular beam, even of the maximum intensity attainable, is thus very attenuated, and its detection and measurement demand technical devices of some refinement. Since the molecules of the beam are moving with thermal velocities, their energy is not sufficient to affect a photographic plate; and since they are neutral, none of the electrometric devices of general application to the detection of beams of charged particles are available. Special methods have therefore had to be devised for molecular beams, none of which has shown itself to be a perfectly general method, equally well adapted to handle all molecular species.

The Condensation Target. The most primitive method

of detection is to place in the path of the beam a metal target, held at a temperature low enough to condense the molecules of the beam as they impinge on it. It is then only a question of time before the beam marks on the target the imprint of its cross-section. The condensation target is, contrary to casual expectation, an extremely sensitive detector within its obviously limited range of application ; for the molecules are not necessarily anchored on the target at the place of impact, but may wander over the surface to form isolated aggregates with other molecules.* It is these molecular aggregates, separated by bare areas of surface, which form the structure of a typical condensate. Thus a deposit shows up on the target far sooner than would be the case if the molecules composing it were uniformly distributed over the surface ; in fact experience shows that a deposit which would be *uniformly* but two or three molecules thick is, thanks to aggregation, actually visible.† On this basis, it is easy to show that the mercury beam discussed above would give a visible deposit in some 10 seconds.

The same fact of molecular aggregation which makes the target so unexpectedly sensitive in the *detection* of molecular beams has prevented it from being more than a semi-quantitative method for their *measurement* ; for the laws connecting the amount of a deposit with such measurable properties as, for example, optical opacity or electrical conductivity are necessarily difficult to establish in view of the complex nature of the condensates.‡ The most generally useful procedure has been to use the time of appearance t of the deposit as an approximate measure of the beam intensity : $I \propto \frac{1}{t}$. Apart from the main disadvantage of its subjective character, this method does not allow the often essential survey of the intensity distribution within a beam.

* See in particular Estermann, *Z. Physikal. Chem.*, **106**, 403, 1923 ; Cockcroft, *Proc. Roy. Soc.*, A, **119**, 293, 1928.
† Estermann and Stern, *Z. Physikal. Chem.*, **106**, 399, 1923.
‡ cf. Lovell, *Proc. Roy. Soc.*, A, **157**, 311, 1936.

2

The condensation target has been always less frequently used as devices able to measure accurately at least relative intensities have been introduced. Fortunately, it is not necessary that the metrical detectors should fulfil the much more stringent demand of determining beam intensities absolutely; for it is always possible to refer the intensity of beams deflected by electric or magnetic fields, or scattered by gases or at solid surfaces, to that of the uninfluenced or parent beam.

Manometers. One of the most widely used groups of metrical devices is that based on the following principle : *
One places athwart the beam a slit or circular aperture according to the profile of the beam, which is the only opening to an otherwise closed vessel containing a sensitive manometer. The beam is allowed entry to the vessel by opening a shutter placed in its path; after a time depending on the volume of the vessel and the molecular weight of the beam species, an equilibrium pressure will be established in the vessel, when as much gas leaves the detector aperture per unit time as the beam brings in. It is this end pressure, or a predetermined fraction of it, which is measured, and which is proportional to the intensity of the beam.

The order of magnitude of the end pressure is readily found. Thus if a, a' are the areas of the source and detector apertures; p, p' the pressures in source and detector, and r the distance between source and detector, then the amount of gas entering the detector per unit time is $\text{const.}\dfrac{p.a.}{\pi r^2}.a'$, that leaving $\text{const.}p'.a'$. For equilibrium

$$p' = p_\infty = \frac{p.a.}{\pi r^2}.$$ Numerically : $p = 1$ mm., $a = 10^{-3}$ cm.^{2}
$r = 10$ cm., whence $p_\infty = 3\cdot2 \times 10^{-6}$ mm.

The equilibrium pressure may be increased considerably by giving the detector aperture the form of a canal.†
The molecules of the beam, being unidirectional, still

---

* Stern, *Z. Physik*, **39**, 759, 1926.
† Knauer and Stern, *Z. Physik*, **53**, 766, 1929.

ave free entry to the detector, but a greater resistance s thereby offered to their unco-ordinated exit at equilirium ; we have $p_\infty = \kappa . \dfrac{pa}{\pi r^2}$. There is however a restriction on the value that can conveniently be given to he multiplication factor, inasmuch as the time needed to each the end pressure is directly proportional to it. A usual value for κ is 10, although by artfully restricting he volume of the detector it has been possible to use uccessfully a κ-factor of 50.[*]

As a general rule, then, one is dealing with pressures f the order of 10^{-5} mm. Thus if one wants to measure he total beam intensity correct to say 1 in 1,000, one must be prepared to measure pressure differences of the rder of 10^{-8} mm. Now the pressure in the observation hamber may easily fluctuate by that amount or more, nd it is therefore very desirable to have a compensation nanometer, built exactly like the measuring manometer s regards volume and κ-factor, placed in the observation hamber but out of range of the beam. Pressure fluctuations in the observation chamber are then automatically alanced out.

Two types of manometer have been used to measure he equilibrium pressure in the detector vessel, and hence he beam intensity : namely the hot-wire gauge and the onization gauge, both of which are linear gauges within he pressure range of actual experiments. The hot-wire gauge utilizes the change of resistance suffered by a hot vire when cooled by the presence of a gas at low pressure, he resistance of the wire being measured in the usual vay by making it one arm of a Wheatstone bridge. This gauge was introduced by Hale [†] and by Pirani,[‡] and was perfected in the hands of Knauer and Stern [§] until capble under the best conditions of measuring changes of

[*] Frisch and Stern, *Z. Physik*, **85**, 4, 1933.

[†] Hale, *Trans. Amer. Electro-Chem. Soc.*, **20**, 243, 1911.

[‡] Pirani, *Deutsch. Phys. Gesell. Verb.*, 1906, p. 684.

[§] Knauer and Stern, *Z. Physik*, **53**, 766, 1929 ; cf. also Knauer, ibid., **80**, 83, 1933.

10^{-9} mm. in a pressure of 10^{-5} mm. It has the general merit of simplicity of construction, and with it the addition of a compensation manometer has the dual advantage both of eliminating stray disturbances and of actually increasing the sensitivity of the arrangement.* It is easy to show that the sensitivity is greater the lower the temperature of the walls of the containing vessel, and the smaller the molecular weight of the beam species. It is, therefore, most suitable for use with light, difficultly condensible gases such as hydrogen and helium, and it has been widely employed over a range of researches with these gases by Stern and his collaborators.†

The ionization gauge can usefully be employed when the beam species is heavier and more readily condensible. So far, however, it has been used comparatively little, mainly for two reasons : it is difficult to give it the small volume necessary to achieve a conveniently short time of filling concurrently with a large κ-factor ; and it is less readily adaptable to compensation than the hot-wire gauge.

The Surface Ionization Detector. Detectors based on the phenomenon of surface ionization have been used in a number of important experiments. They are linear, extremely sensitive, and delightfully easy to use, and it is unfortunate that their range of application is severely restricted, namely to substances with very low ionization potentials.

The phenomena of surface ionization on which this method of detection rests are briefly these : Atoms which impinge on a hot surface are in general adsorbed and re-evaporated, either as neutral atoms or as positive ions. The ratio of the number of ions n^+ to neutrals $n^\times$ leaving the surface per second is

$$\frac{n^+}{n^\times} = e^{-F(I-\phi)/RT} \qquad . \quad . \quad . \quad (1.4$$

* Hale, loc. cit.

† cf. Fraser, *Molecular Rays*, pp. 34–42, where a detailed account of the use of manometers in molecular beam technique is given

‡ Johnson, *Phys. Rev.*, **31**, 103, 1928 ; Ellett and Zabel, ibid, **37**, 1112, 1931 ; Huntoon and Ellett, ibid., **49**, 381, 1936.

where I is the ionization potential of the atom, ϕ the work function of the surface, and F the Faraday number. If $I - \phi \sim -0.5$ volt, $n^\times$ is negligible, and practically all the atoms evaporate as ions. With tungsten ($\phi = 4.48$ volts) as solid surface, this condition is fulfilled for potassium, rubidium, and caesium, whose ionization potentials are all around 4 volts. Lithium (5.37 volts) and sodium (5.13 volts) already require oxygenated tungsten ($\phi \sim 7$ volts) for a certainty of surface ionization.* Thus only beams of one or other of the alkali metals (or their halides) † can be detected by this means.

The surface ionization gauge was first used to measure the intensity of alkali metal beams by Taylor, working in Stern's laboratory.‡ He placed a hot tungsten wire, surrounded by a negatively charged cylinder, in the path of the beam, and measured the saturated ionization current between wire and cylinder. It is quite a large current; thus, using the estimate of the beam intensity found at page 6, we see that the saturation current from a wire 5 mm. long and 0.01 mm. wide is

$$10^{11}.1.6 \times 10^{-19} = 1.6 \times 10^{-8} \text{ amps.}$$

Thus the sensitivity of the arrangement is very high; a great reserve is moreover at hand, since it is possible to use the method ballistically, collecting the atoms for as much as several minutes on a cold wire, then suddenly flashing off the accumulated deposit.

The Space-Charge Detector. The detectors so far discussed, the condensation target, the manometers, and the surface ionization detector alike, are only capable of handling each a limited range of molecular species. We come finally to describe a detector which, potentially at any rate, is of universal application. The principles underlying the use of this, the space-charge detector, are as follows: The electron emission from a hot wire placed in the axis of a positively charged cylinder is, if the anode

* Langmuir and Kingdon, *Proc. Roy. Soc.*, **A**, **107**, 61, 1925.
† Rodebush and Henry, *Phys. Rev.*, **39**, 386, 1932.
‡ Taylor, *Z. Physik*, **57**, 242, 1929.

potential and relative dimensions of wire and cylinder are suitably chosen, governed by the negative space charge around the cathode.* If gas is admitted to the region between wire and cylinder, the molecules are ionized by electron bombardment from the wire, at sufficiently high anode voltage ; the positive ions so formed are attracted to the cathode, where they partially neutralize the negative space charge, causing an increase in the emission current. The effect is greatly increased by closing the two ends of the cylindrical anode, except for two small holes through which the wire passes. The positive ions are then trapped for a considerable time in the box so formed.† Under these conditions, a pressure of 10^{-8} mm. of mercury vapour may cause an increase in the emission current of as much as 0·1 milliamps.

Estermann and Stern ‡ have adapted the 'Kingdon Cage' to the measurement of beam intensities, using mercury as test substance. The beam enters the box through a small aperture, setting up an equilibrium pressure of which the increase in electron emission is a measure. It is, of course, necessary to hold the anode potential above the ionization potential of the beam species, otherwise the entering beam will not in the least affect the electron emission from the cathode ; but since each and every molecule is ionizable, the detector is potentially of universal application. Moreover the anode, already fairly hot through radiation from the negative filament, can readily be maintained at a still higher temperature ; and hence beams of heavy, easily condensible molecules are open to measurement, particularly in view of the fact that the sensitivity of the gauge increases with increasing molecular weight of the beam species.§

In its present form, the cage has a small κ-factor, determined by the ratio of the areas of the beam aperture to all the openings in the cage : namely 0·1 to 0·01. Thus

* cf. Appleton, *Thermionic Vacuum Tubes* in this Series, p. 21.
† Kingdon, *Phys. Rev.*, **21**, 408, 1923.
‡ Estermann and Stern, *Z. Physik*, **85**, 135, 1933.
§ Kingdon, loc. cit.

the equilibrium pressure lies between 10^{-8} mm. and 10^{-7} mm., which is nevertheless well within the useful range of what is clearly an exceptionally sensitive device. There is, however, the disadvantage that the relation between equilibrium pressure and increase in emission

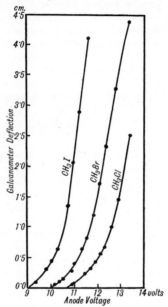

FIG. 2.—Curves showing Ionization Potentials of Methyl Halides CH₃Cl, 10·7; CH₃Br, 10·0; CH₃I, 9·1 volts ± 0·25.

current is not linear, the gauge being more sensitive at lower pressures.

The space-charge detector has been little used so far in work with molecular beams, but its wide range of application is nicely illustrated by Jewitt's determinations of ionization potentials, which will therefore be described here. Jewitt * made molecular beams of formaldehyde

* Jewitt, *Phys. Rev.*, **46**, 616, 1934.

and certain methyl halides, which were shot into a Kingdon cage, the emission current of which was balanced
out by a compensation gauge placed beside it in the
observation chamber and in the adjacent arm of an electrical bridge. Increase of emission current on entry of
the beam to the measuring cage was consequently read
directly as a galvanometer deflection. By plotting galvanometer deflection against anode voltage, the ionization
potential was obtained by extrapolation of the resulting
curve to zero deflection, the voltage scale being first cali-
brated against mercury, assuming the spectroscopic value
(10·4 volts) for the ionization potential of that substance.
Jewitt's measurements for the methyl halides are seen in
fig. 2; they are in good agreement with Price's more
recent and exact values, obtained optically.*

* Price, *Phys. Rev.*, **47**, 419; 510, 1935; *J. Chem. Phys.*, **4**,
359, 1936.

CHAPTER II

GAS KINETICS

IN the paper describing his pioneer experiments,[*] Dunoyer wrote : ' La possibilité d'observer un rayonnement material dont l'énergie est d'origine entièrement thermique ouvre la voie à un assez grand nombre de recherches, dont l'ensemble pourrait porter le nom de *cinétique expérimentale*.' Although Dunoyer did not himself follow up his suggestion, his prediction has been fulfilled by others, and experimental gas kinetics is now an increasingly important application of the molecular beam method. The first real impetus to research in this direction was given by Stern's direct determination of thermal velocities in 1920,[†] followed in 1929 by Lammert's verification of the Maxwell distribution law.[‡]

The ultimate aim of Stern's measurements was towards an experimental study of the departures from classical gas kinetic theory adumbrated at the time by the developing quantum theory. The wave mechanics had, of course, not yet been formulated, and it has since become clear that Stern's original plan—a direct search for a departure from the Maxwell distribution of velocities—is experimentally almost hopeless.[§] Nevertheless, a new and fruitful line of investigation, the scattering of molecular beams in gases, was indicated by wave theory, and largely owing

* Dunoyer, *Compt. rend.*, **152**, 595, 1911.
† Stern, *Z. Physik*, **2**, 49, 1920 ; **3**, 416, 1920.
‡ Lammert, *Z. Physik*, **56**, 244, 1929 ; see also Eldridge, *Phys. Rev.*, **30**, 931, 1927.
§ cf. Lenz, *Z. Physik*, **56**, 778, 1929.

to experience in the use of the quantitative detectors described in the last chapter, considerable advances have
already been made.

The New Gas Kinetics. Some of the most striking
points of difference between the new gas kinetics and
classical nineteenth-century theory emerge at once from
a consideration of collision phenomena in gases, using the
simplest possible molecular model, the hard sphere.

On classical theory, the direction of the relative velocity
of two hard spheres before collision may, by the fact of
collision, be turned through any angle θ with equal probability.* In other words, all angles of scattering θ are
equally likely. The cross-section effective in collision is
$Q = \pi r_0^2$, where $r_0 = r_1 + r_2$ is the sum of the radii of
the colliding molecules.

In wave-mechanical theory, the collision of two hard
spheres is pictured as the scattering at a perfectly opaque
sphere of radius r_0 of a plane matter-wave of wavelength
$\lambda = \dfrac{h}{Mv}$; v is the relative velocity of the spheres before
collision, $M = \dfrac{m_1 m_2}{m_1 + m_2}$ the 'reduced mass'. On this
picture, the square of the amplitude of the scattered wave
at the surface of a large sphere, in whose centre the molecules collide, gives the probability of scattering in any
particular direction.

Now if the wavelength λ is very large in comparison
with the radius r_0 of the sphere of action, in other words
if the relative velocity before collision is small, then the
probability of scattering is once more the same for all
angles of scattering ; but the effective collision cross-
section is $4\pi r_0^2$ in place of the classical value πr_0^2.

If, on the other hand, $\lambda \ll r_0$ (relative velocity large),
then the scattering function is no longer uniform over
all angles of scattering. Instead, there is an extremely
high probability of scattering for very small angles about
the forward direction ; for larger angles, it is of the same

* Jeans, *The Dynamical Theory of Gases*, 4th Ed., 1925, p. 260

average magnitude as that to be expected classically (cf. fig. 3). The effective collision cross-section is in this case $2\pi r_0{}^2$.

In cases intermediate between these two extremes, there

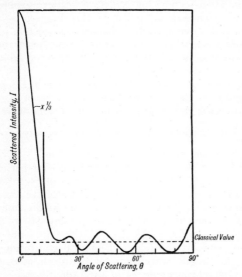

FIG. 3.—Angular Distribution of Helium Atoms scattered by Helium Atoms at 20° K, after Massey and Mohr

will always be preference for forward scattering, for angles of scattering smaller than $\theta = \frac{1}{2} \cdot \frac{\lambda}{r_0}$; the smaller θ, the more intense the scattering within that angle (cf. fig. 3).

Thus even qualitatively, the predictions of classical and of quantum (wave-mechanical) theory of the collision of hard spheres are vastly different. It is interesting to note, however, that in some respects the conclusions drawn from the quantum theory for hard spheres simulate those of the classical theory of a more complicated molecular model, that of hard spheres exerting attraction at a distance. With this model, classical theory also predicts a preference for scattering in a forward direction, but with this important distinction: that any classical theory involving attraction at a distance leads to an infinite collision cross-section for angles of scattering approaching zero; whereas on quantum theory, even assuming attraction at a distance, the collision cross-section remains finite (although in such case with a value larger than the hard sphere limit of $2\pi r_0{}^2$) provided the force falls off at large distances r faster than r^{-3}.*

Diffraction of Molecular Beams. Now the essential assumption in the wave-mechanical picture of the collision process is the assignment of a de Broglie wavelength $\lambda = \dfrac{h}{mv}$ to particles of mass m and velocity v. This assumption has, of course, an enormous body of evidence behind it, but its most vivid confirmation for particles of atomic mass came from the experiments of Stern and his collaborators on the diffraction of molecular beams at crystal surfaces. These experiments are fundamental, and we shall review them first before passing on to discuss the experiments on molecular scattering in gases which so nicely support the newer theoretical conclusions.

The de Broglie wavelength of hydrogen at $0°$ C., to take a concrete example, is of the order

$$\lambda = \frac{h}{mv} = \frac{6\cdot54 \times 10^{-27}}{3\cdot3 \times 10^{-24}.1\cdot7 \times 10^5} = 1\cdot2 \times 10^{-8} \text{ cm.}$$

that is, of the same order as that of X-rays. Hence it was likely *a priori* that just as X-rays are diffracted at the three-dimensional grating of a crystal lattice, so molecular rays should be diffracted at the two-dimensional grating of a cleavage plane. But first one had to consider whether a beam of molecules can be specularly

---

* A full account of the new theories of collision processes is given in Mott and Massey's *Theory of Atomic Collisions*, Oxford, 1933. See in particular Chapter XIII, § 3; or Massey and Mohr, *Proc. Roy. Soc.*, A, **141**, 434, 1933 (hard-sphere model); ibid., **144**, 188, 1934 (hard spheres with attraction at a distance) for the original sources.

reflected at a crystal surface, for without specular reflection no regular diffraction pattern is possible.

Now in optics the condition for specular reflection is simply this : that the height of the inequalities of the surface projected on the direction of the beam of light should be less than one wavelength.* Clearly this condition is satisfied for a beam of say hydrogen ($\lambda \sim 1$ Å) falling sufficiently obliquely on the cleavage plane of a perfect crystal, which is rendered matt to the extent of about an Ångstrom by the temperature oscillation of the ions.† In the case of molecular beams, however, the optical condition for specular reflection, while necessary, is not sufficient : there is a second condition, namely that the time of adsorption of the particles of the beam on the surface should be vanishingly short. If this condition is not fulfilled, then however smooth the surface there is random scattering of the beam.‡ Nor must we forget that beams of heavy particles of short de Broglie wavelength, such as mercury, may simulate specular reflection by bouncing off the surface like elastic balls.§ It appears that true specular reflection is confined to beams of gases with low critical points, such as hydrogen, the inert gases, and atomic hydrogen.||

The conditions for specular reflection fulfilled, we may consider what sort of diffraction pattern is to be expected when a molecular beam falls on the cleavage face of a cubic crystal such as NaCl. The rows of ions in the surface form a rectangular cross-grating, therefore the diffracted beams must satisfy the equations

$$\left. \begin{array}{l} \cos \alpha = \cos \alpha_0 \pm h_1.\lambda/d \\ \cos \beta = \cos \beta_0 \pm h_2.\lambda/d \end{array} \right\} \quad \cdot \quad \cdot \quad \cdot \quad (2.1)$$

* cf. Wood, *Physical Optics*, 2nd Ed., 1923, p. 42.

† Knauer and Stern, *Z. Physik*, **53**, 786, 1929 ; Estermann and Stern, ibid., **61**, 115, 1930 ; Johnson, *J. Franklin Inst.*, **207**, 635, 1929 ; ibid., **210**, 145, 1930.

‡ Taylor, *Phys. Rev.*, **35**, 375, 1930 ; Cohen and Ellett, *Phys. Rev.*, **51**, 65, 1937 (A).

§ Josephy, *Z. Physik*, **80**, 755, 1933 ; also for citations of the relevant literature.

|| Eisenschitz and London (*Z. Physik*, **60**, 516, 1930) have deduced theoretically the critical data of atomic hydrogen.

Here α_0, β_0 are the angles between the incident beam and the x and y axes of the grating ; α, β the angles made by the diffracted beam with these axes ; d is the grating spacing ; and h_1, h_2 are whole numbers.*

We identify the x axis with a row of similar ions in the cleavage face,† and consider the first order spectra

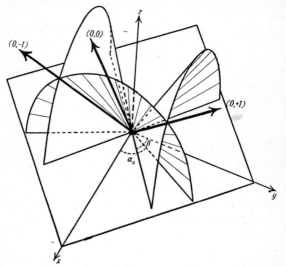

Fig. 4.—Illustrating the Diffraction of a Molecular Beam at the Surface of a Crystal

($h_1 = 0$, $h_2 = \pm 1$) from a beam incident in the xz plane ($\beta_0 = 90°$) ; then the diffracted beams all lie on a cone of semi-vertical angle $\alpha = \alpha_0$ about the x axis. For any one de Broglie wavelength λ, the first order (0, ± 1) diffracted beams will lie right and left of the directly reflected beam (0, 0 order), at the intersections of the α-cone with the β-cones for which $\cos\beta = \pm\,\lambda/d$. But the incident beam is not monochromatic in λ ; rather,

* cf. Fraser, *Molecular Rays*, p. 98 ff.
† Stern, *Naturwiss.*, **17**, 319, 1929.

ne velocities of the molecules are governed by the Max-
ell distribution in the source. Hence we should expect
he first order diffracted beams to be spread out into a
ontinuous spectrum around the α-cone, with a maximum
f intensity at the most probable wavelength (fig. 4).

These predictions are beautifully fulfilled in the pioneer
xperiments of Estermann and Stern,* and in the further
xperiments by Estermann, Frisch, and Stern,† which
atter we shall describe here as being the simpler. A

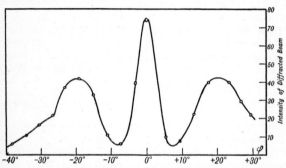

FIG. 5.—Intensity of diffracted Beams of Helium Atoms plotted
gainst Angle of Rotation φ of a LiF Crystal (Estermann, Frisch,
and Stern)

beam of helium atoms of circular cross-section is incident
at a cleavage surface of LiF, oriented as in fig. 4. The
eceiving canal of a hot-wire gauge detector is adjusted
n the xz plane so as to make the same angle with the
crystal as the incident beam, thus admitting the directly
reflected beam (0, 0 order). The crystal is now rotated
about the x axis, when the (0, 1 order) diffracted beams
corresponding to the continuously varying values of λ in
the incident beam are admitted in succession to the fixed
receiver.

In fig. 5 the intensity of the diffracted beam is plotted

* Estermann and Stern, Z. Physik, **61**, 95, 1930.
† Estermann, Frisch and Stern, Z. Physik, **73**, 348, 1931.

against the angle of rotation ϕ of the crystal ($\lambda = 2d.|\sin\phi$.sin α_0). One glance at the figure tells that the main features of the predicted pattern are fulfilled.*

The same is true of fig. 6, (frontispiece), due to Johnson.† Here a beam of atomic hydrogen is incident at a LiF crystal oriented as in fig. 4 ; the diffracted beams are received on a target coated with the pale yellow MoO_3 which is reduced to the blue-black MoO_2 by the impinging hydrogen atoms. This arrangement has the qualitative advantage of giving a simultaneous record of the complete diffraction pattern : intense directly reflected beam, imprint of the α-cone, degenerate β-cone (xz plane) for which $h_2 = 0$.

Stern's results, however, contain more than a general direct verification of the existence of molecular de Broglie waves ; they give complete quantitative confirmation of the de Broglie relation $\lambda = \dfrac{h}{mv}$. The confirmation rests, in the case we are considering, on the identification of the maxima at $\phi = 19°$ (fig. 5) with the (0, ± 1) order diffracted beams corresponding to the wavelength λ present in greatest intensity in the incident beam.

Thus if dn is the instantaneous number of molecules in the source with velocities between v and $v + dv$, the direction of v being identified with the axis of the beam,

---

* The irregularity in the otherwise smooth curve, occurring between $\phi = 20°$ and $\phi = 30°$ is real, appearing strongly, with other such, in apparatus of higher resolving power (Frisch and Stern, *Z. Physik*, **84**, 430, 1933). Frisch (ibid., **84**, 443, 1933) showed that all the anomalies could be described phenomenologically by assuming a preferential adsorption of particles impinging at the crystal with particular components of momentum relative to the surface. Frisch's formulation has recently received a brilliant theoretical interpretation at the hands of Lennard-Jones and Devonshire (Lennard-Jones and Devonshire, *Nature*, **137**, 1069, 1936 ; Devonshire, *Proc. Roy. Soc.*, A, **156**, 37, 1936), which has at the same time indicated a wide field for future experiment.

† Johnson, *Phys. Rev.*, **35**, 1299, 1930 ; *J. Franklin Inst.*, **210**, 135, 1930.

then the number of such molecules arriving on unit area per second is

$$dI = v.dn \quad . \quad . \quad . \quad . \quad (2.2)$$

where I is the total intensity of the beam. Now, by the Maxwell law,

$$dn = C.e^{-v^2/\alpha^2}.v^2.dv \quad . \quad . \quad . \quad (2.3)$$

where $\alpha = \sqrt{\dfrac{2RT}{M}}$ is the most probable velocity of the molecules in the source.

Therefore

$$dI = C'.e^{-v^2/\alpha^2}.v^3.dv \; ; \quad C' = \frac{2I}{\alpha^4} \quad . \quad . \quad (2.4)$$

a relation already verified in Stern's laboratory by Lammert.* Changing the independent variable in equation (2.4) from v to $v = \dfrac{h}{m\lambda}$, we have

$$dI = C''.e^{-\lambda\alpha^2/\lambda^2}.1/\lambda^5.d\lambda \quad . \quad . \quad (2.5)$$

whence it follows that $\lambda_m = \sqrt{\dfrac{2}{5}}.\lambda_\alpha = \sqrt{\dfrac{2}{5}}.\dfrac{h}{m\alpha} = \dfrac{1.95 \times 10^{-7}}{\sqrt{MT}}$ cm.

This then is the wavelength to be associated with the maxima of the (0, 1) diffraction spectra. Calculation shows it should occur, in the case we have been considering, at an angle of rotation of the crystal $\phi = 18°$. Observed, $\phi = 19°$.

Molecular Scattering in Gases. Before the advent of the molecular beam method, mean free paths and molecular collision cross-sections were usually determined in either of two ways, namely by observation of gaseous viscosity or diffusion. The importance of the beam method lies in the fact that it does not merely offer an alternative to the other two. It has a wider range than either. Thus comparing the expressions for the collision cross-section derived from the theory of all three methods :

* Lammert, Z. Physik, 56, 244, 1929.

3

$$Q_\eta = 2\pi \int_0^\pi I(\theta).\sin^3\theta.d\theta \left.\begin{array}{c} \\ \\ \\ \end{array}\right\}$$

$$Q_D = 2\pi \int_0^\pi I(\theta).\sin^2\tfrac{1}{2}\theta.\sin\theta.d\theta \quad . \quad . \quad (2.6)$$

and

$$Q_B = 2\pi \int_0^\pi I(\theta).\sin\theta.d\theta$$

in which $I(\theta)$ is the scattering function relating the probability of scattering to the angle of scattering θ : we see that the value Q_B of Q derived from the theory of scattering of a molecular beam, unlike the quantities Q_η and Q_D, depends on the *first power* only of $\sin\theta$. Physically, this means that the beam method counts as a collision a molecular encounter far less intimate than that needed for the exchange of energy and momentum in amounts sufficient to influence the viscosity or rate of diffusion of a gas. Clearly therefore the important region of very small angles of scattering,* to which the standard methods are quite insensitive, is open for detailed examination by the beam method, and moreover over a far wider range of substances.

Early experiments already gave a pointer in this direction. Thus Knauer and Stern † observed in 1926 that the intensity of a mercury beam was reduced to about an eighth of its vacuum value in traversing some 12 cm. of air at a pressure of 10^{-4} mm., a reduction which corresponds to an atomic radius at least twice as large as the then accepted gas kinetic radius ; while later, from observation of the loss in intensity suffered by a considerably narrower beam of hydrogen traversing a hydrogen-filled chamber, they obtained a value for the mean free path of hydrogen in hydrogen only 0·44 times that derived from standard viscosity measurements.‡ The mere fact that small values for the mean free path (and consequently large values for the effective collision cross-section) are obtained when small angles of scattering are counted, is,

* Compare p. 17 above.
† Knauer and Stern, *Z. Physik*, **39**, 764, 1926.
‡ *Ibid*, **53**, 766, 1929.

however, not in itself an unequivocal test of the theoretical conclusions discussed earlier in this chapter. One must be able to say whether the collision cross-section tends to a *large but finite*, or to an *infinite* value for zero angle of scattering.

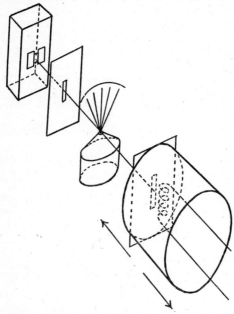

FIG. 7.—Illustrating Broadway's Experiments on the Scattering of Alkali Metal Beams

A first step in this direction was made by Broadway,* using the method of crossed molecular beams developed by Fraser and Broadway.† His arrangement is seen schematically in fig. 7. A ribbon-shaped beam of alkali metal atoms, formed *in vacuo* in the usual way by source and image slits, passes close above the circular opening of an oven from which mercury is streaming molecularly.

* Broadway, *Proc. Roy. Soc.*, A, **141**, 634, 1933.
† Fraser and Broadway, *Proc. Roy. Soc.*, A, **141**, 626, 1933.

The density of the mercury stream is so adjusted tha[t] the alkali metal atoms suffer single collisions in traversin[g] it. The alkali metal beam is received at a surface ioniza[tion] gauge, the aperture of which is defined by a sl[it] placed in front of the coiled anode. The gauge can b[e] traversed *in vacuo* in the direction of the beam, in th[is] way presenting to it a larger aperture at forward position[s] of the gauge, a smaller at backward positions. The ang[le] range covered is from $1 \cdot 0°$ to $0 \cdot 2°$, which latter angle [is] well within the critical range of scattering $0 < \theta < \frac{1}{2} . \lambda /$[a] for sodium and potassium scattered by mercury.

Broadway's procedure was as follows : First the inten[-] sity I_0 of the primary beam, with the mercury strea[m] frozen out, was noted at a series of positions of the dete[c-] tor ; next, the intensity $I'(\theta)$ of the beam, weakened b[y] passage through the mercury stream, was determined a[t] the same series of positions of the detector ; and henc[e] the ratio $I'(\theta)/I_0$ for any angle of scattering within th[e] range observable is found.

Now with Broadway's arrangement, to a sufficientl[y] good approximation,

$$I'(\theta) = I + 2 \int_0^\theta I(\theta) . d\theta \quad . \quad . \quad . \quad (2.7)$$

where $I(\theta)$ is the scattered intensity per unit solid angl[e] for an angle of scattering θ, and I the corresponding inten[-] sity for vanishingly small angles of scattering.* Henc[e] extrapolation of the curves relating $I'(\theta)/I_0$ with θ to zer[o] angle yields $I/I_0 = e^{-d/\lambda}$, if λ is the mean free path [of] the alkali metal atoms traversing an effective width d [of] mercury vapour of predetermined density.

Thus to a finite value of Q corresponds a positive frac[-] tional value of I/I_0. In fig. 8, the circles represent Broad[-] way's experimental points for the system sodium-mercury[,] the full line the curve to be expected theoretically if $I(\theta)$ in (2.7) is set equal to $e^{-\theta^2}$, an expression which for sma[ll] values of θ approximates closely to the form of the scatter[-] ing curve derived by Massey and Mohr (fig. 3).† Th[e]

* Fraser, Massey, and Mohr, *Z. Physik*, **97**, 740, 1935.
† *Ibid.*, loc. cit.

greement is tolerably good, and demonstrates neatly the
ndamental distinction between classical theory with
traction at a distance $(I/I_0 \rightarrow o)$ and the predictions of
ave mechanics $(o < I/I_0 < 1)$.

A more refined study of small angle scattering is that
ue to Rabi and his collaborators Mais and Rosin.* The
pparatus used by Rosin and Rabi is illustrated schematic-

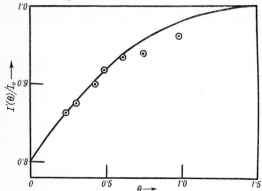

FIG. 8.—Scattering of Sodium by Mercury (Broadway)

lly in fig. 9. An alkali metal beam is formed in the
sual way by the slit-shaped aperture of the oven (1) and
ne image slit (2). It is scattered in the small volume
ormed at the constriction (3) of the scattering chamber
4), to which a variety of gases can be admitted from a
as reservoir via the tube (5); (6) leads to a McLeod
auge, at which the pressure of the scattering gas is meas-
red. The beam is received on a straight tungsten fila-
nent (7), 0·02 mm. in diameter, which subtends an angle
f only 1·7 minutes of arc at the scattering chamber.
The filament forms the anode of a surface ionization
auge, and can be traversed across the beam by rotating
ne ground joint to which the gauge is attached, thus
iving a point-to-point plot of the beam profile.

* Mais, *Phys. Rev.*, **45**, 773, 1934; Rosin and Rabi, ibid.,
8, 373, 1935.

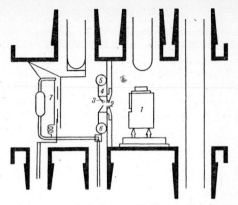

Fig. 9.—Apparatus of Rosin and Rabi for the Measurement of Collision Cross-Sections

1. Oven for vaporizing Alkali Metal. 2. Image Slit. 3. Scattering Volume. 4. Scattering Chamber. 5. Gas Inlet. 6. to McLeod Gauge. 7. Tungsten Filament.

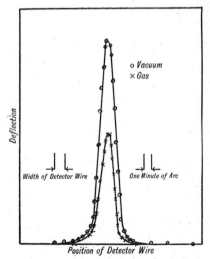

Fig. 10.—Scattering of Sodium by Argon (Rosin and Rabi)

A typical plot is seen in fig. 10. Purely qualitatively it is very instructive. It will be noticed that the beam which has been weakened by scattering is indistinguishable in profile from a vacuum beam of lower intensity; it has not been observably broadened by scattering. This means that at high angular resolution (here one minute of arc) a finite limit of the mean free path for zero angle of scattering is indeed being approached.

This conclusion is confirmed by the quantitative evaluation, from the relative values of the peak intensities, of the effective collision cross-section. The most recent data are set out in Table I, which is taken from Rosin and Rabi. Selecting the values for potassium scattered at helium, neon, and argon; namely

$$7\cdot25 \qquad\qquad 9\cdot10 \qquad\qquad 13\cdot6\,\text{Å}$$

respectively, we compare them with the corresponding values

$$6\cdot91 \qquad\qquad 8\cdot74 \qquad\qquad 13\cdot0\,\text{Å}$$

obtained by Mais with beams effectively four and a half times as wide: an agreement which points with final conviction to a finite value of the total collision cross-section.

The data of Table I are already sufficiently extended to reveal many points of detail for theory to work on. Possibly the most important is the trend of the r_0 values in the series helium, neon, and argon; for whereas the

TABLE I

VALUES OF EFFECTIVE COLLISION CROSS-SECTIONS Q AND RADII r_0
FOR THE ALKALI ATOMS IN VARIOUS GASES

Gas	Lithium		Sodium		Potassium		Rubidium		Caesium	
	r_0	Q	r_0	Q	r_0	Q	r_0	Q	r_0	Q
H_2	6·21	122	7·01	154	7·47	175	7·38	171	7·54	179
D_2	6·32	125	7·62	182	8·54	228	8·24	213	8·34	219
He	5·82	106	6·44	130	7·25	165	6·96	152	7·18	162
Ne	6·18	120	8·24	213	9·10	259	9·23	268	9·56	287
A	9·83	303	11·3	401	13·6	580	13·5	572	13·5	572

The collision radii are expressed in Ångstroms and cross-sections in square Ångstroms.

values observed with helium show good agreement with those to be expected on the quantum theory of hard spheres, both neon and argon are found to possess even larger cross-sections. It is clear, therefore, that for them the hard-sphere model is already too simple, and that an additional attraction at a distance must be assumed.

Now Massey and Mohr * have shown that in this case

$$Q = \pi \cdot \frac{2s - 3}{s - 2} \cdot f^{2/(s-1)} \cdot \left(\frac{C'}{k}\right)^{2/(s-1)} \quad . \quad . \quad (2.8)$$

where $k = \dfrac{2\pi M v}{h}$, M being as usual the reduced mass; $C' = \dfrac{8\pi^2 M.C}{h^2}$, such that the potential $V(r) = -\dfrac{C}{r^s}$; and f is a function of s only.

There are two ways in which this equation may be used to determine the force constant C. The first way is to *assume* that the van der Waals potential energy of interaction of two atoms at a distance r is $- C.r^{-6}$, an assumption for which there is good theoretical evidence; then $s = 6$ in (2.8), and measurement of Q at a single temperature (in other words, for one value of v) suffices to determine C. Examples of the use of this procedure are to be found in the paper of Fraser, Massey and Mohr already cited, and in a recent letter by Massey and Buckingham.†

The second way of applying equation (2.8) needs no initial assumption regarding the value of s. Thus it is clear that $Q \propto T^{-1/(s-1)}$; hence measurement of the variation of Q over a considerable range of temperature would determine s; s known, the value of C follows at once. There is ample material here for future experiments; and already tentative observations of the influence of temperature on the scattering of molecular beams have been made by Knauer ‡ and by Zabel.§

* Massey and Mohr, *Proc. Roy. Soc.*, A, **144**, 187, 1934.
† Massey and Buckingham, *Nature*, **138**, 77, 1936.
‡ Knauer, *Naturwiss.*, **21**, 366, 1933; *Z. Physik*, **90**, 559, 1934.
§ Zabel, *Phys. Rev.*, **46**, 410, 1934.

CHAPTER III

MAGNETIC MOMENTS

ATOMIC MAGNETIC MOMENTS

IN a magnetic field of strength H, an atom possessing a magnetic moment μ suffers a change of energy

$$\Delta W = \mu_H . H \quad . \quad . \quad . \quad . \quad (3.1)$$

where μ_H is the component of μ in the direction of the field. If we identify the position of the atom with the origin of an arbitrary set of co-ordinates x, y, z, then the force acting on the atom in, say, the x direction is $F_x = \partial W/\partial x$. Differentiating (3.1) with respect to x, and remembering that μ_H is constant provided the atom cannot gain energy from sources, such as radiation or collision, other than the field, we have

$$F_x = \mu_H . \frac{\partial W}{\partial x} \; ; \; F_y = \mu_H . \frac{\partial W}{\partial y} \; ; \; F_z = \mu_H . \frac{\partial W}{\partial z} . \quad (3.2)$$

Thus in a homogeneous magnetic field

$$(F_x = F_y = F_z = 0)$$

there is no force on the atom due to the field. If, however, the field is inhomogeneous, as for example near a wedge-shaped pole-piece (fig. 11), where to a good approximation $F_x = F_y = 0$ in or near the plane of symmetry xz, then an atom shot into the field suffers an acceleration in the z direction of amount

$$f = \frac{F_z}{m} = \mu_H/m.(\partial H/\partial z) \quad . \quad . \quad . \quad (3.3)$$

An atom shot along the length l of the wedge-shaped pole-piece with velocity v will therefore suffer a deflection s of amount

$$s = \tfrac{1}{2}.f.t^2 = \tfrac{1}{2}.f.l^2/v^2 = \tfrac{1}{4}.\mu_H.(\partial H/\partial z).l^2/\varepsilon_v \quad (3.4)$$

where ε_v is the translational energy corresponding to v.

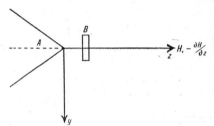

FIG. 11.—The Stern-Gerlach Experiment
A—Section of Pole-piece. B—Profile of Beam

Now for an atom in a given ^rL_j state,* μ_H can take only certain discrete values, namely

$$\mu_H = M.g.\mu_0 \quad . \quad . \quad . \quad . \quad (3.5)$$

where μ_0 is the natural unit of magnetic moment, the Bohr magneton ($\mu_0 = 0.918 \times 10^{-20}$ erg gauss^{-1}); M is integral or half-integral according as J is integral or half-integral, and assumes the $2J + 1$ equally probable values defined by the relation $- J \leftrightharpoons M \leftrightharpoons J$; and g is the Landé factor, given, for states governed by Russell-Saunders coupling, by

$$g = 1 + \frac{J(J + 1) + S(S + 1) - L(L + 1)}{2J(J + 1)} \quad (3.6)$$

whereby $L = 0, 1, 2 \ldots$ for S, P, D $\ldots$ states, and S is derived from the multiplicity r according to the scheme $r = 2S + 1$.

Thus for a $^2S_{\frac{1}{2}}$ state, for example, which is the ground

---

* See Pauling and Goudsmit, *Structure of Line Spectra*, New York, 1930, for a particularly clear account of the ^rL_j classification of atomic energy states.

state of all the members of Group I of the Periodic Table, we have $M = \pm \frac{1}{2}$, $g = 2$; and from (3.4) and (3.5)

$$s = \pm \tfrac{1}{4}.\mu_0.(\partial H/\partial z).l^2/\varepsilon_v \quad . \quad . \quad . \quad (3.7)$$

A beam of alkali metal atoms, or of silver atoms, will therefore split into two in traversing a sufficiently inhomogeneous magnetic field; taking $\partial H/\partial z = 10^4$ gauss/cm., $l = 10$ cm., $\varepsilon_v = k\text{T} = 1.37 \times 10^{-16}$ ergs at $1,000°$ K, the splitting $2s$ of a beam of silver atoms of velocity v at the exit of the field will be of the order 5×10^{-1} mm.

Stern-Gerlach Experiment. This was actually the result obtained in 1921-2 by Gerlach and Stern * in the celebrated Stern-Gerlach experiment. The experiment has often been described, and here we need only refer to the fuller accounts to be found, for example, in Fraser's *Molecular Rays* or Stoner's *Magnetism and Matter*.

The result was, of course, both quantitatively and qualitatively, a complete vindication of the predictions of quantum theory; but it is often forgotten that the experiment was undertaken, not merely to give a sort of demonstration experiment of the space quantization postulated by the spectroscopists, but chiefly because on the basis of the then current Bohr-Sommerfeld atom model, the theory led to an apparent contradiction in the field of optics. Thus Stern,† who first drew attention to the paradox, pointed out that a gas composed of oriented, highly asymmetrical atoms would be expected to show magnetic double refraction at all wavelengths. Special investigations undertaken by Fraser ‡ and by Schütz § with sodium vapour showed not the slightest trace of such an effect; while Fraser ‖ found that the mean free path of atomic hydrogen canal rays in argon was the same whether a magnetic field were imposed in the direction of the beam or not. These experiments showed, in fact, that

* Gerlach and Stern, *Ann. Physik*, **74**, 673, 1924.
† Stern, *Z. Physik*, **7**, 249, 1921.
‡ Fraser, *Phil. Mag.*, **1**, 885, 1926.
§ Schütz, *Z. Physik*, **38**, 854, 1926.
‖ Fraser, *Proc. Roy. Soc.*, A, **114**, 212, 1927.

the atoms of sodium and hydrogen are spherically symmetrical; a result which was, of course, in complete accord with the contemporaneous findings of Schrödinger's theory.

In other words, Stern's paradox was resolved by the more developed atom model of wave mechanics; all the experimental results fell into line, and it was no longer difficult to reconcile the physical splitting of an atomic beam with the absence of optical asymmetry in a magnetized gas.

Magnetic Deflection Patterns. Table II shows the deflection patterns to be expected from equations (3.4), (3.5), and (3.6) for some normal states of frequent occurrence, assuming a single velocity beam. A molecular beam, however, possesses a velocity spectrum determined by the Maxwell distribution of velocities in the source, and the components of an actual deflection pattern will in consequence be broad bands rather than sharp lines. It is therefore necessary to consider how far the resolving power of the Stern-Gerlach arrangement is affected thereby.*

TABLE II

Normal State	g	Mg	Deflection Pattern
$^1S_0$	$\frac{0}{0}$	0	
$^2S_{\frac{1}{2}}$	2	$-1 \quad +1$	
$^2P_{\frac{1}{2}}$	$\frac{2}{3}$	$-\frac{1}{3} \quad +\frac{1}{3}$	
$^3P_0$	$\frac{0}{0}$	0	
$^3P_1$	$\frac{3}{2}$	$-\frac{3}{2} \, 0 + \frac{3}{2}$	
$^3P_2$	$\frac{3}{2}$	$-3 - \frac{3}{2} \, 0 + \frac{3}{2} + 3$	
$^4S_{\frac{3}{2}}$	2	$-3 - 1 \quad +1 + 3$	

We have seen (Chapter II, p. 23) that the fraction $I(v)dv$ of the total beam intensity I_0 arising from those molecules with velocities between v and $v + dv$ is given by the equation

$$I(v)dv = \frac{2I_0}{\alpha^4}.e^{-v^2/\alpha^2}.v^3.dv \quad . \quad . \quad (3.8)$$

Now from (3.7), $s \propto 1/v^2$; hence changing the independent variable in (3.8) from v to $s = s_\alpha.\alpha^2/v^2$, s_α being the deflection corresponding to the most probable velocity α, we get

$$I(s)ds = \tfrac{1}{2}.I_0.e^{-s_\alpha/s}.s_\alpha^2/s^3.ds \quad . \quad . \quad (3.9)$$

as the intensity between s and $s + ds$ in either of the two deflected beams into which a beam of atoms with $J = \tfrac{1}{2}$ splits (cf. Table II).

Implicit in (3.9) is the assumption that the width of the parent beam is negligible in comparison with that of its deflected components. If on the other hand we assume the parent beam to have a rectangular intensity distribution of width $2a$, (3.9) becomes

$$I_s = \tfrac{1}{2}.I_0\left[F\left(\frac{s_\alpha}{s+a}\right) - F\left(\frac{s_\alpha}{s-a}\right) \right] \quad . \quad (3.10)$$

whereby $F(x) = (1 + x)e^{-x}$.

A graphical plot of equation (3.10) is shown in fig. 12. Curve O, the profile of the parent beam at the position of the detector, is replaced by the dotted rectangle in accordance with the assumption made in deriving (3.10), $2a$ being now identified with the half-width of the parent beam. Curve I, the actual intensity distribution in a deflected component, is repeated in Curve II on ten times the ordinate scale.

In evaluating μ^H from such an intensity curve, one first determines s_α, when μ_H follows from (3.7) with ε_v set equal to kT. There are several possible ways of finding s_α, of which we need consider at present only two: (1) A metrical detector for the particular beam species is available: the position of maximum intensity s_m is determined and s_α obtained from (3.10), subject to the condition $dI/ds = 0$. (2) A metrical detector is not available. This has actually been the case for most of the atoms investigated, for which the target detector only was applicable. An example of a deflection pattern obtained on a cooled target is seen in fig. 13, (frontispiece). Here the limits of visibility s_1, s_2 of the deflected trace, for which $I_1 = I_2$, are measured, substituted in turn in (3.10), and the resulting expressions in s_α and s_1 or s_2 respectively equated.

So far we have confined our attention to a splitting into two components only. There may, however, be four or

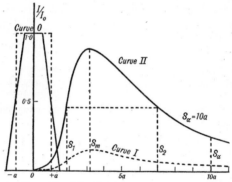

FIG. 12.—Intensity Distribution in a Deflected Component

more deflected components in a magnetic deflection pattern (Table II). The case of four components, all deflected ($J = \frac{3}{2}$), is illustrated in fig. 14, which shows one half only of the symmetrical deflection pattern. It will be seen that the intensity curves arising from the single components $Mg = 1$ and $Mg = 3$ overlap, giving a summation curve with but a single maximum. Thus a beam of, for example, bismuth atoms splits into *two* deflected beams only, the individual components being unresolved, and it is therefore necessary to know the J-value of the normal state of the atoms from spectroscopic data, before the deflection pattern can be interpreted.

This proviso applies, of course, equally to those deflection patterns which are genuinely composed of two components ; for only by a previous knowledge that the r-value of the normal state is $\frac{1}{2}$ could one be certain that they too were not composite.

The independent scope of the beam method is thereby severely limited, and the determinations which have been made of the magnetic moments (or better Mg-values) of different atoms must in the main be regarded as confirmation of existing spectroscopic data rather than independent determinations.

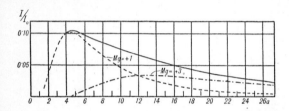

FIG. 14.—Summation Curve of two Deflected Components, with the Mg-values $+ 1$ and $+ 3$

Mg-Values. A list of the Mg-values hitherto obtained by the beam method is set out in Table III* (on page 38). Two entries in the table require some comment, namely bismuth and atomic oxygen.

In the case of bismuth, it will be noticed that there is a discrepancy between the Mg-values listed in the third and fourth columns. This is because the spectroscopic Mg-values have been calculated on the assumption of Russell-Saunders coupling, whereas in a heavy atom like bismuth Stoner coupling is to be expected.† Mg-values are in general unpredictable for Stoner coupling, except in a special case like bismuth, where, for extreme Stoner

* Details of technique and interpretation of results are given in Fraser, *Molecular Rays,* Chapter V.
† cf. Hund, *Linienspektren,* Berlin, 1927 ; § 38, p. 182.

TABLE III

Atom	Normal State	Mg		Authors
		Spectroscopic	Beam	
H	$^2S_{\frac{1}{2}}$	± 1	± 1	Phipps and Taylor, *Phys. Rev.*, **29**, 309, 1927; Wrede, *Z. Physik*, **41**, 569, 1927.
Li.	$^2S_{\frac{1}{2}}$	do.	do.	Taylor, *Z. Physik*, **52**, 846, 1929.
Na, K	$^2S_{\frac{1}{2}}$	do.	do.	Taylor, *Phys. Rev.*, **28**, 576, 1926;
Cu, Ag, Au	$^2S_{\frac{1}{2}}$	do.	do.	Leu, *Z. Physik*, **41**, 551, 1927.
Zn, Cd, Hg	$^1S_0$	0	0	Gerlach, *Ann. Physik*, **76**, 163, 1925.
Tl	$^2P_{\frac{1}{2}}$	$\pm \frac{1}{3}$	$\pm \frac{1}{3}$	Leu, loc. cit.
Sn, Pb	$^3P_0$	0	0	Leu, loc. cit.
Bi	$^4S_{\frac{3}{2}}$	$\pm 1, \pm 3$	$\pm 0 \cdot 72, \pm 2 \cdot 16$	Gerlach, loc. cit. Leu and Fraser, *Z. Physik*, **49**, 498, 1928.
O.	$^3P_{2,1,0}$	—	—	Kurt and Phipps, *Phys. Rev.*, **34**, 1357, 1929.
Pd	$^1S_0$	0	0	Guthrie and Copley, *Phys. Rev.*, **38**, 360, 1931.

coupling, they turn out to be 0·67 and 2·01, in reasonable agreement with the values found by Leu and Fraser.

Atomic oxygen, received on a litharge target, was found to give an undeflected trace and two deflected traces. The deflected traces are very complex (cf. Table III, also Table II), but giving proper weight to the various states present, a mean μ_H-value of 1·71 μ_0 is predictable from spectroscopic data. Kurt and Phipps obtained μ_H (mean) = 1·67 μ_0.

NUCLEAR SPINS AND MAGNETIC MOMENTS

The restrictions on the independent scope of the beam method of measuring atomic magnetic moments are not in principle inescapable. Thus one could first produce a beam of restricted velocity range before sending it through the field, for example by means of a system of rotating sectors.* The deflection pattern would then display a series of separate maxima, the number of which, $(2J + 1)$, would determine J, their separation g. That this frequently discussed extension of the technique has not been applied to the measurement of atomic moments is due, partly to the practical difficulties of velocity selection, but chiefly to the fact that the J-values and Mg-values of the atomic ground-states have been so firmly established both by spectroscopic theory and by the completely concordant measurements of the Zeeman effect that an independent series of determinations by another method has seemed superfluous.

It is otherwise with nuclear spins and magnetic moments. Their determination by spectroscopic methods requires a detailed analysis of the hyperfine structure of spectral lines : † always a matter of considerable difficulty, and sometimes, as when the lines to be analysed lie far out

---

* cf. Lammert, *Z. Physik*, **56**, 244, 1929 ; Estermann, Frisch and Stern, ibid., **73**, 348, 1931.

† See article by Bethe and Bacher, *Reviews of Modern Physics*, **8**, 82, 1936.

in the ultra-violet, impracticable with the technical methods so far available. An independent check on the spectroscopic values is therefore most desirable, and this the beam method can give ; more, it is sometimes applicable in cases where spectroscopic methods fail.

The first step in this direction was taken by Breit and Rabi.* They pointed out that if I is the angular momentum, or spin, of the nucleus in units of $h/2\pi$, J that of the external electron configuration, then in a magnetic field which is weak enough to allow the coupling of the I and J vectors to be maintained there occur $(2I + 1)(2J + 1)$ magnetic levels. In other words, a 'monochromatic' beam sent through a *weak* inhomogeneous magnetic field (of the order of ten to a hundred gauss) will show $(2I + 1)(2J + 1)$ peaks. Knowing J, the mere counting of these peaks determines I. Breit and Rabi pointed out, further, that the separation of the peaks might be used to determine the nuclear magnetic moment μ_N.

Their suggestion was carried into effect by Rabi and Cohen,† for the case of sodium. A Stern-Gerlach pattern was produced in the usual way by sending a beam of sodium atoms through a *strong* inhomogeneous magnetic field. A selector slit placed well out on the skirt of one deflected beam permitted a limited range of the slowest atoms only to pass on to a long *weak* inhomogeneous field. Here the coupling between I and J was maintained, contrary to the situation in the first, velocity selecting field. The selected beam, after passage through the weak field, was received at a surface ionization detector, used ballistically. The deflection pattern seen in fig. 15 was obtained on traversing the detector wire through the selected beam. The peak at A is due to some fast atoms from the scattered tails of the initial beam which the selector slit has allowed to pass ; it is therefore not to be counted in with the others. There are thus four peaks, and since $J = \frac{1}{2}$ and only *half* the fine structure deflection

   * Breit and Rabi, *Phys. Rev.*, **38**, 2082, 1931.

   † Rabi and Cohen, *Phys. Rev.*, **43**, 582, 1933 ; ibid., **46**, 707, 1934.

pattern is obtained by the method of velocity selection used, we have

$$\tfrac{1}{2}.(2I + 1).2 = 4$$

whence $I = \tfrac{3}{2}$.

The Alkali Metals. The method of Breit and Rabi in its first most direct form was almost immediately super-

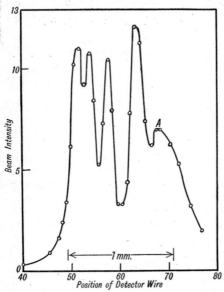

Fig. 15.—Deflection of Sodium Atoms in a weak Magnetic Field (Rabi and Cohen)

seded by a powerful modification of it, which follows at once from the detailed quantitative development of their original ideas. The method of zero moments, as it has been called by Rabi, requires no initial 'monochromatization' of the beam, and is moreover superior in resolving power to its parent. It has been applied successfully to the determination of the nuclear spins and magnetic moments of all the alkali metals.

Thus for any alkali metal atom, possessing as it does a doublet S ground-state ($J = \frac{1}{2}$), the force on the atom in a weak inhomogeneous magnetic field, such that the interaction between the nuclear and electronic spins is maintained, is given by

$$\left.\begin{aligned}
F_z &= \mp \frac{2m/(2I+1)+x}{2(1+[4m(2I+1)]x+x^2)^{\frac{1}{2}}} \cdot \mu_0 \cdot \frac{\partial H}{\partial z} \\
&= f_m \cdot \mu_0 \cdot \partial H/\partial z
\end{aligned}\right\} \quad (3.11)$$

$$x = 2\mu_0 . H/h.c.\Delta\nu \quad . \quad . \quad . \quad (3.12)$$

Here m is the *total* magnetic quantum number, that is the projection of the total angular momenta $F = I \pm \frac{1}{2}$ of the two energy states present in zero external field or the field direction H; for example, if $I = \frac{3}{2}$ we have

F	1	2
and m	— 1, 0, 1 ;	— 2, — 1, 0, 1, 2 ;

each of the $2(2I+1)$ values of m being equally probable. $\Delta\nu$ is the energy difference in wave numbers between the two states defined by $F = I \pm \frac{1}{2}$. f_m is clearly the effective magnetic moment of the atom in the magnetic level m, in units of the Bohr magneton μ_0. h and c are, of course, Planck's constant and the velocity of light respectively.

It is clear from (3.11) that f_m *vanishes* for those values of x which satisfy the relation

$$x = -2m/(2I+1) \quad . \quad . \quad . \quad (3.13)$$

and in Table IV are set out the values of x for which f_m equals zero for a series of values of the nuclear spin. The contents of the table are exhibited graphically for

TABLE IV

$I =$	$\frac{1}{2}$	$\frac{2}{2}$	$\frac{3}{2}$	$\frac{4}{2}$	$\frac{5}{2}$	$\frac{6}{2}$	$\frac{7}{2}$	$\frac{8}{2}$	$\frac{9}{2}$
$f_m = 0$ when $x =$	0	0·333	0·5	0·6	0·667	0·714	0·75	0·777	0·
			0	0·2	0·333	0·429	0·50	0·555	0·
					0	0·143	0·25	0·333	0·
							0	0·111	0·
									0·

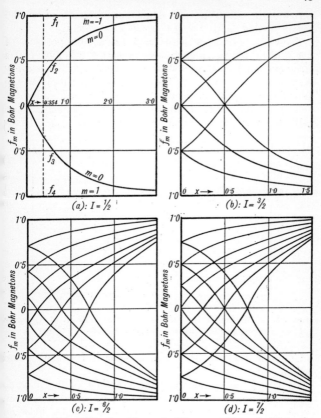

FIG. 16.—The Effective Magnetic Moments (f_m) of Atoms in the different magnetic levels of a $^2S_{\frac{1}{2}}$ ground state, plotted against
$$x = (2\mu_0/hc\Delta\nu)H$$

the cases $I = \frac{1}{2}$, $\frac{3}{2}$, $\frac{6}{2}$ and $\frac{7}{2}$ in figs. 16A to 16D. The figures show, moreover, how on passing to strong fields the $2(2I + 1)$ values of f_m coalesce to the two values ± 1 in every case : all influence of the nuclear spin I disappears, and we are left with just the Mg-values characterizing the electron spin which are determined in the usual (strong field) Stern-Gerlach experiment.

Now suppose a detector stationed at the position of the undeflected beam at the exit of a weak inhomogeneous magnetic field ($x < 1$). With zero field there is in every case a maximum value of the intensity, due simply to the uninfluenced primary beam. Keeping the position of the detector fixed, and gradually increasing the field, there will be no further maxima observed if $I = \frac{1}{2}$, one further

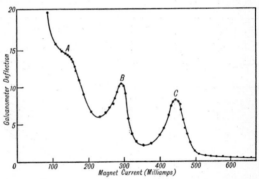

FIG 17.—Variation of Intensity at $s = 0$ of a Beam of Caesium Atoms, plotted against Magnet Current (Cohen)

maximum if $I = \frac{2}{2}$ or $\frac{3}{2}$, two maxima if $I = \frac{4}{2}$ or $\frac{5}{2}$ and so on.

If $I > \frac{3}{2}$ the number and the x-*position* of the maxima is alone necessary to determine I, for the x-interval between zero and the first peak for even spins is half that between successive peaks, whereas for odd spins the intervals are equal throughout (cf. figs. 16c and 16D).

Fig. 17 shows a plot of the beam intensity at $s = 0$ against field strength for the case of caesium.* The three *equally* spaced peaks A, B, and C fix I unambiguously as $\frac{7}{2}$.

If $I = \frac{3}{2}$, it is necessary to measure the *intensity* of the single peak relative to that of the primary beam, in order

* Cohen, *Phys. Rev.*, **46**, 713, 1934.

to decide between the alternatives $I = \frac{2}{2}$ and $I = \frac{3}{2}$. Since each of the $2(2I + 1)$ m-levels is equally probable, and since at the peak *two* of these states have zero moment simultaneously, the intensity at the peak will be $1/(2I + 1)$ that of the primary beam : namely, $\frac{1}{3}$ if $I = \frac{2}{2}$, $\frac{1}{4}$ if $I = \frac{3}{2}$. In this way, Millman* determined the nuclear spin of the principal potassium isotope K^{39} as $\frac{3}{2}$; while Fox and Rabi† determined the nuclear spins of Li^7 and Na^{23}, also as $\frac{3}{2}$.

That the method can be used, if the resolution is adequate, to determine the nuclear spins of the individual isotopes, for which I and μ_N naturally differ, was pointed out by Rabi.‡ In the experiments of Millman already mentioned, a small peak due to K^{41} was in fact observed ; and later Manley§ was able to determine the nuclear spin of the isotope as $\frac{3}{2}$. Rb^{85} and Rb^{87} have recently been examined by Millman and Fox.‖

So much for the determination of the nuclear spin I ; but the nuclear magnetic moment μ_N can also be evaluated if the wave functions of the atom under examination are sufficiently well known.

Thus in virtue of (3.12) the value of the field at any one of the peaks suffices to determine Δv. Now

$$\Delta v = (32\pi/hc).\mu_N.\mu_0.\psi^2(o) \quad . \quad . \quad . \quad (3.14)$$

where $\psi(o)$ is the value of the wave function at the nucleus. If $\psi(o)$ is known, μ_N follows at once from a knowledge of Δv. The order of magnitude of μ_N is, of course, some two-thousandths that of the Bohr magneton ; for we must replace the electron mass m in the expression $\mu_0 = (e/2mc).(h/2\pi)$ by a mass of the same order as that of the proton. It is customary, therefore, to express μ_N in terms of the nuclear magneton $\mu_s = 1/1838.\mu_0$.

The values of I and μ_N which have so far been deter-

* Millman, Fox, and Rabi, *Phys. Rev.*, **46**, 320, 1934 ; Millman, ibid., **47**, 739, 1935.
† Fox and Rabi, *Phys. Rev.*, **48**, 746, 1935.
‡ Rabi, *Phys. Rev.*, **47**, 334, 1935.
§ Manley, *Phys. Rev.*, **49**, 921, 1936.
‖ Millman and Fox, *Phys. Rev.*, **50**, 220, 1936.

mined by the methods outlined above are collected in Table V.

These results, apart from being based on most ingenious methodics, are due to technical achievement of the highest quality. Thus in order to obtain the resolution necessary to show up the peaks narrow slits and beams as long as a couple of metres are used. This entails on the one hand extremely accurate adjustment, on the other the measurement of very feeble intensities at the detector : thus using the surface ionization gauge ballistically, times of collection on the cold filament of the order of 10 minutes have been necessary. Finally, the very long weak fields, possessing a high inhomogeneity which is constant over the height of the beam, have been obtained by a cunning arrangement of current carrying wires, the characteristics of the field being known completely from the geometry of the arrangement.

The Proton and the Deuteron. The spins of the proton and the deuteron are known from observation of the *molecular* spectra of hydrogen and deuterium to be $\frac{1}{2}$ and 1 respectively : values which have recently been confirmed by a molecular beam method by Rabi and his co-workers.*

On the other hand, a spectroscopic determination of their magnetic moments fails, owing to the fact that the lines which would give the required information lie far out in the ultra-violet, and have never been resolved. The measurement of these quantities, so fundamental for nuclear theory, by Stern in 1933 and by Rabi in 1934 is thus an outstanding instance of the power of the beam method.

Stern and Rabi adopted two different procedures : Stern measured the deflection of *molecular* hydrogen in a strong magnetic field, Rabi that of *atomic* hydrogen in a weak field. We consider Stern's method first.

Ordinary $H_2{}^1$ is a mixture of para-hydrogen (proton spins opposed, zero nuclear moment, rotation states 0, 2, 4 . . .) and orthohydrogen (proton spins parallel, nuclear moment $2\mu_P$, rotation states 1, 3, 5 . . .) in the ratio 1 : 3.

* Kellogg, Rabi, and Zacharias, *Phys. Rev.*, **50**, 472, 1936.

TABLE V

Substance	I in units of $\frac{h}{2\pi}$	μ_N in units of μ_s	Reference
Li (6)	1	0·85	Fox and Rabi, *Phys. Rev.*, **48**, 746, 1935; Manley and Millman, ibid., **50**, 380, 1936.
Li (7)	3/2	3·28	Fox and Rabi, loc. cit.
Na (23)	3/2	2·08	Rabi and Cohen, *Phys. Rev.*, **46**, 707, 1934; Fox and Rabi, loc. cit.
K (39)	3/2	0·40	Millman, *Phys. Rev.*, **47**, 739, 1935; Fox and Rabi, loc. cit.
K (41)	3/2	0·22	Manley, *Phys. Rev.*, **49**, 921, 1936.
Rb (85)	5/2	1·44	Millman and Fox, *Phys. Rev.*, **50**, 220, 1936.
Rb (87)	3/2	2·92	Millman and Fox, loc. cit.
Cs	7/2	2·82	Cohen, *Phys. Rev.*, **46**, 713, 1934; Millman and Fox, loc. cit.

Pure para-hydrogen at $90°$ K is 98 per cent in the state $J = 0$; experimentally, it was found to have zero moment, the beam being undeflected in a field of $\partial H/\partial s \sim 2 \cdot 10^5$ gauss/cm. On the other hand, pure para-hydrogen at $195°$ K is 73 per cent in the state $J = 0$, 27 per cent in the state $J = 2$; experimentally the undeflected beam ($J = 0$) was now found to have deflected spurs ($J = 2$), measurement of which gave the moment μ_R arising from the rotation of the molecule as a whole. The deflection suffered by a beam of ordinary H_2^1 at $195°$ K could now be analysed as arising from the superposition of deflected beams due to μ_R alone (para-hydrogen in the state $J = 2$) and both μ_P and μ_R (ortho-hydrogen). In this way, Stern and his collaborators * made the remarkable discovery that μ_P has the value, not one nuclear magneton, μ_s, but $2 \cdot 5 \pm 0 \cdot 25$ μ_s.

By a quite analogous procedure, the magnetic moment of the deuteron was found to be $0 \cdot 7$ nuclear magnetons.†

Rabi and his co-workers have used two distinct methods, the beam in each case being of atomic hydrogen. The first method ‡ is based directly on the theory outlined in the preceding section concerning the alkali metals. The ground state of atomic H^1 is $^2S_{\frac{1}{2}}$; thus $J = I = \frac{1}{2}$, and the variation with x of the resulting four values of f_m in (3.11) are as graphed in fig. 16A. Ideally, a monochromatic beam of H^1 sent through a weak field H would show four *equidistant* lines when $x = 0 \cdot 354$; the value of H at which this is the case would then at once determine $\Delta \nu$ and hence μ_P.

However, to obtain the complete pattern it would be necessary to use a mechanical velocity selector, since the magnetic velocity analyser can, as we have seen, yield only half the full pattern. In view of this complication, together with the fact that no detector of the extreme

* Frisch and Stern, *Z. Physik*, **85**, 4, 1933; Estermann and Stern, ibid.

† Estermann and Stern, *Z. Physik*, **86**, 132, 1933; *Nature*. **133**, 911, 1934.

‡ Rabi, Kellogg, and Zacharias, *Phys. Rev.*, **46**, 157, 1934.

sensitivity necessary was available for atomic hydrogen, Rabi, Kellogg and Zacharias contented themselves with an ordinary beam having Maxwellian velocity distribution, the beam after passage through the weak field being received on a molybdenum oxide target. The magnetic pattern consisted of *two* deflected traces, since the independent traces due to f_1 and f_2, f_3 and f_4 overlap in pairs ; however, the field strength H was given the smallest possible value consistent with a clear splitting of the parent beam, so that the inner components arising from f_2 and f_3 should contribute as markedly as possible to the width of the summation traces.

The procedure adopted in determining μ_P from the characteristics of the deflected traces was then closely analogous to that followed in determining the electronic moment of bismuth (see p. 37 and particularly fig. 14) : The limits of visibility s_1, s_2 of the summation traces are determined. Since $s_\alpha.(f_1) = s_\alpha.(f_4)$ are field independent and attributable to the electron spin only, $s_\alpha.(f_2) = s_\alpha.(f_3)$ can be deduced. Knowing $s_\alpha.(f_2)$, $f_2 = x/(1 + x^2)^{\frac{1}{2}}$ follows (equation 3.7), then $\Delta\nu$ from (3.12) ; whence finally μ_P from (3.14), since $\psi(0)$ is known exactly for the hydrogen atom. In this way, μ_P was found to be $3\cdot25 \pm 0\cdot32$ nuclear magnetons.

The same apparatus, and a similar analysis of the deflection pattern, gave for the deuteron moment $0\cdot75 \pm 0\cdot2$ nuclear magnetons.*

Rabi's second and more precise method,† in which incidentally the detection of the beam is made objective by the use of a hot-wire gauge detector, depends on focusing, by means of a strong inhomogeneous magnetic field, the separate components of a beam of atomic hydrogen which has already passed through a weak magnetic field. In the weak field, the beam is split into $2(2I + 1)$ (unresolved) components ; if now the strong field is arranged to produce deflections in opposite directions to those imposed by the weak field, the $2(2I + 1)$ components may be

* Rabi, Kellogg, and Zacharias, *Phys. Rev.*, **46**, 163, 1934.
† Kellogg, Rabi, and Zacharias, *Phys. Rev.*, **50**, 472, 1936.

brought to a focus in pairs (for atomic hydrogen f_1, f_4 and f_2, f_3 (fig. 16A)) on the line $s = 0$, $l = l'$, irrespective of the velocity distribution of the atoms in the primary beam.

Thus in the first place, the intensity at $s = 0$, for a fixed position of the Stern-Pirani detector, when plotted as a function of the first deflecting field H, will show $(2I + 1)$ peaks ; in this way the spins of the proton and the deuteron have been established as $I = \frac{1}{2}$ (two peaks) and $I = 1$ (three peaks) respectively.

In the second place, the H-values at these peaks allow a calculation of the H.F.S. separation $\Delta\nu$ and hence of μ_N. By this method, Kellog, Rabi and Zacharias find $2\cdot85 \pm 0\cdot15\mu_s$ and $0\cdot85 \pm 0\cdot30\mu_s$ for the magnetic moment of the proton and the deuteron respectively.

The values of μ_P and μ_D in units of μ_s, found by the three methods just discussed, are collected in Table VI.

TABLE VI

	Stern		Rabi	
	First values	Revised values *	First method	Second method
μ_P :	$2\cdot5 \pm 0\cdot25$	$2\cdot5 \pm 0\cdot25$	$3\cdot25 \pm 0\cdot32$	$2\cdot85 \pm 0\cdot15$
μ_D :	$0\cdot7$	$0\cdot85$ to $0\cdot90$	$0\cdot75 \pm 0\cdot20$	$0\cdot85 \pm 0\cdot30$
μ_P/μ_D :	$3\cdot6$	$(2\cdot94)$	$4\cdot3$	$3\cdot35$

* Privately communicated.

It will be seen that the discrepancies between the first results of Stern and Rabi have been considerably reduced by the later, more accurate experiments. The major disparity now lies, not so much between the results of the beam method, as between the beam values of the ratio μ_P/μ_D and the value $3\cdot96 \pm 0\cdot11$ found by Farkas and Farkas * from the relative rates of the ortho-para-hydrogen conversion for hydrogen and deuterium.

* Farkas and Farkas, *Proc. Roy. Soc.*, **A, 152,** 152, 1933 ; cf. also Bethe and Bacher, loc. cit., p. 218.

In any event, the result which is vastly more important than any discrepancy is the assignment to the proton of a magnetic moment greater than unity ; for it means that the g-value of the proton is not 2, that of the electron, and hence that the proton is not describable by the Dirac wave equation which describes the electron. In other words, the proton is almost certainly not a simple particle. These are obviously conclusions of fundamental importance.

The Sign of the H and D Nuclear Moments. The sign of a nuclear moment may be deduced from the character of the hyperfine structure multiplets : if these are ' regular ' the nuclear moment is positive, if ' inverted ', negative.* Since, as we have already remarked, the hyperfine structure of the Lyman lines has not so far been resolved, the spectroscopic method can say nothing directly about the sign of the proton moment : that is, whether the magnetic moment is in the same direction as the angular momentum (positive moment) or in the opposed direction (negative moment). The same is true of the deuteron nuclear moment.

Nor can a simple deflection experiment, even if performed with a weak field, give the information sought ; for the deflection patterns (see fig. 16) are in all cases completely symmetrical. Quite recently, however, Rabi † has devised means by which it is, in fact, possible to determine the sign of any nuclear moment *including that of the proton.*

The method is based on a closer interpretation and extension of experiments carried out in Stern's laboratory in Hamburg by Phipps and Stern ‡ and Frisch and Segré.§ The idea of these experiments is as follows : A beam of potassium atoms is sent through a strong inhomogeneous magnetic field and the ordinary Stern-Gerlach deflection pattern is obtained. A selector slit permits one branch

* cf. Bethe and Bacher, loc. cit., Chapter VIII.
† Rabi, *Phys. Rev.*, **49**, 324, 1936.
‡ Phipps and Stern, *Z. Physik*, **73**, 183, 1931.
§ Frisch and Segré, *Z. Physik*, **80**, 610, 1933.

only of the pattern to enter a magnetically shielded region in which obtains a very weak field, whose direction, originally that of the first strong field, changes through a predetermined angle over a short distance. The selected beam then passes out of the shielded region into a second strong inhomogeneous magnetic field, whose direction coincides with the final direction of the weak intermediate field. Analysis of the beam emerging from the final field with a surface ionization gauge answers the question whether the atoms of the selected beams have maintained their orientation, acquired in traversing the deflecting field, or whether some of them have reversed their orientation in the weak intermediate field.

It turns out that if the rate of change of direction of the weak field is small compared with the Larmor frequency $\omega = 2\pi.g.\mu_0.H/h$, the atoms maintain the orientation acquired in the deflecting field; if on the other hand it is comparable with the Larmor frequency, then a certain proportion of the atoms can change their orientation.* This is just the result obtained in the final experiments of Frisch and Segré; and Rabi has shown that their data receive complete quantitative interpretation if the effect of the nuclear spin of the potassium atoms, which is, of course, strongly coupled to the electron spin in the weak intermediate field, is taken into account.

The way in which these experiments can be adapted to determine the sign of a nuclear moment, in particular that of the proton, was indicated by Rabi as follows: Since the spins of electron and proton are both $\frac{1}{2}$, the two energy states of the hydrogen atom present in zero external magnetic field are $F = 0$ and $F = 1$; hence the states arising in an external field are given by the scheme

$$F: \qquad 0 \qquad\qquad\qquad 1$$
$$m: \qquad 0 \qquad\qquad -1 \quad 0 \quad 1$$

The variation of f_m with field, as calculated from (3.11)

* Güttinger, *Z. Physik*, **73**, 169, 1931; Majorana *Nuovo. Cim.* **9**, 43, 1932. See also Motz and Rose, *Phys. Rev.*, **50**, 348, 1936.

first on the assumption of a positive proton moment, secondly of a negative moment, is seen in figs. 18 A and B, where the dotted lines denote the state arising from F = o, the full lines those arising from F = 1.

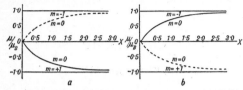

Fig. 18.—Variation of Effective Moment f_m with Field, for the Case $J = \frac{1}{2}$, $I = \frac{1}{2}$.

The dotted lines correspond to the state F = o, m = o; the full lines to the states F = 1, m = o ± 1
In (a) the nuclear moment is assumed to be positive, in (b) negative.

A beam of atomic hydrogen sent through a *weak* deflecting field will consist of two branches, the state $m = o$ arising from F = o being in the branch deflected towards or away from the stronger part of the inhomogeneous field according as μ_P is positive or negative. Thus a selector slit placed at the inner edge of the branch deflected towards the stronger field permits either (a) atoms in the state F = o, $m = o$ or (b) those in the state F = 1, $m = o$ to pass to the weak intermediate field. Now this field is so weak that no transitions are possible between states with different F-values, but only between m-states having the same F-value. Thus on passing to the *strong* analysing field, the selected beam will have a single maximum in case (a), but two maxima in case (b), since a transition is possible between the state (F = 1, $m = o$) and (F = 1, $m = 1$), which is oppositely deflected. Just the reverse is true if the selector slit is placed at the inner edge of the branch deflected towards the weaker part of the deflecting field.

The experiments have been carried through by Kellogg, Rabi and Zacharias * for both proton and deuteron. In each case the moment is positive.

* Kellogg, Rabi, and Zacharias, loc. cit.

CHAPTER IV

ELECTRIC MOMENTS

MOLECULES are built up of positive and negative particles, and the finished structure is symmetrical in widely varying degree. The centre of gravity of the positive nuclei of the constituent atoms may or may not coincide with that of all the extra-nuclear electrons : in the first case, the molecule is non-polar ; in the latter, polar. Polar molecules possess a *permanent* electric moment μ_ϵ, the order of magnitude of which is readily estimated, thus : $\mu_\epsilon = e.r$, where e is of the order of the electronic charge, $4 \cdot 77 \times 10^{-10}$ E.S.U., and r that of a molecular diameter, 10^{-8} cm. ; giving $\mu_\epsilon \sim 10^{-18}$ E.S.U., or 1 Debye. Whether the molecule has a permanent dipole moment or not, it will, since the electronic structure is not rigid, achieve an *induced* moment $\mu_i = \alpha.E$ when placed in an electric field E. The polarizability α is commonly of the order 10^{-24} E.S.U. ; so that in a field of 150,000 volts per cm., or 500 E.S.U., $\mu_i \sim 5 \times 10^{-22}$ E.S.U.

Electric dipole moments are usually determined by measurements of the dielectric constant of the substance in bulk.* The method depends essentially on observation of the variation of the dielectric constant with temperature, either on the pure substance as gas or vapour, or on its dilute solution in a non-polar solvent. Now the first method demands considerable gaseous pressures before reasonably accurate measurements of the dielectric constant are possible ; and in many, in fact the vast

* Debye, *Polar Molecules*, New York, 1929.

majority of cases, the temperature necessary to give the required vapour pressure is either of itself inconveniently high, or else leads to molecular decomposition. The second method, the so-called 'solution temperature method' necessarily entails a non-polar solvent, which cannot always be found. Moreover, there is the awkward circumstance, only recently brought to light, that the measured value of the total molecular polarization is related, hitherto obscurely, to the dielectric constant of the 'indifferent' solvent, itself of course a temperature dependent quantity.*

The relatively difficult molecular beam technique is free from these complications. The principle of the method lies, of course, in close analogy to the magnetic case, in observing the deviation suffered by a molecular beam when shot through an inhomogeneous electric field. Thus on the one hand the highest vapour pressures ever required in the source are of the order of a millimetre ; on the other, the necessity for a non-polar solvent is removed. A notable example of the use of the method is the case of pentaerythritol, a substance insoluble in non-polar solvents. In 1929 Estermann † showed that a beam of pentaerythritol molecules was strongly deflected in an inhomogeneous electric field, indicating a dipole moment of the order of 2×10^{-18} E.S.U. : a result of considerable theoretical interest at the time. Fig. 19 (frontispiece) shows the traces obtained on a cooled target placed in the path of the beam, to the left that without, to the right that with field.

The accurate determination of electric dipole moments by the molecular rays method, however, demands ineluctably a detector capable of measuring relative intensities. The deflection pattern in the electric case is much less directly interpretable than the analogous pattern for magnetic atoms, and that on account of the temperature rota-

---

* Müller, Jenkins : Faraday Society Discussion at Oxford on Dipole Moments, April, 1934.

† Estermann, *Z. Physikal. Chem.*, **B, 2,** 287, 1929 ; cf. also Estermann and Wohlwill, ibid., **20,** 195, 1933.

tion of the molecules.   Now kinematically there are three main types of molecules : the linear rotator, the symmetrical top, the asymmetrical top.   Accordingly we shall outline something of the theory of the first two groups, relate their behaviour in an electric field to the deflection pattern to be expected, and describe such experiments with metrical detectors as have been carried out with them.

The Linear Rotator.   The type molecule in this class is HCl, which to a first approximation may be represented by a rigid dumb-bell.   Here the direction of the dipole

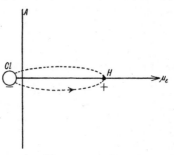

Fig. 20.—Illustrating Temperature Rotation of HCl, (Linear Rotator ; $I_A = I_B$, $I_C = 0$)

moment is in the line joining the two nuclei, and the dumb-bell rotates about an axis A perpendicular to this line (fig. 20).   Such a molecule when shot into an electric field E suffers an instantaneous change of energy

$$\Delta W = \mu_E.E \quad . \quad . \quad . \quad . \quad (4.1)$$

where μ_E is the component of μ_e in the direction of the field.   But the molecule is executing a uniform temperature rotation about the axis A, whose period is short compared with the time the molecule takes to traverse the field in a deflection experiment.   Hence μ_E changes sign every half-period, whatever the inclination of μ_e to the field direction, and the time-averaged energy change

$\overline{\Delta W}$ vanishes to the first order. Thus to the same order the molecule is unaffected by its passage through the field.

The presence of the field, however, perturbs the uniform rotation of the dumb-bell, giving rise to a time-averaged moment $\bar{\mu} = \beta.E$ proportional to the field strength.* Thus to the second order

$$\overline{\Delta W} = \tfrac{1}{2}.\beta.E^2 \quad . \quad . \quad . \quad . \quad (4.2)$$

Now according to quantum theory, ΔW can take a series of certain discrete values only, determined by the rotational quantum number $J = 0, 1, 2 \ldots$, and the equatorial quantum number M, such that $-J \rightleftharpoons M \rightleftharpoons J$. That is, β is a function $\beta(J,M)$ of the quantum numbers J and M. The values of $\bar{\mu} = \beta(J,M).E$ were obtained independently by Mensing and Pauli † and by Kronig.‡ They are

$$\left. \begin{aligned} \bar{\mu} &= \frac{8\pi^2.I_A.\mu_\epsilon{}^2.E}{h^2}.f(J,M) \\[2mm] (J,M) &= \frac{1}{(2J-1)(2J+3)}.\left(\frac{3M^2}{J(J+1)} - 1\right) \; (J \neq 0) \\[2mm] &= \tfrac{1}{3} \qquad\qquad\qquad\qquad\qquad\qquad (J = 0) \end{aligned} \right\} (4.3)$$

where I_A is the moment of inertia of the dumb-bell about the A axis, and h is Planck's constant.

For large values of J (high temperature), (4.3) takes the form

$$\bar{\mu} = \frac{\mu_\epsilon{}^2.E}{4\varepsilon_r}.(3\cos{}^2\phi - 1) = \frac{\mu_\epsilon{}^2.E}{4kT}.(3\cos{}^2\phi - 1) \; (4.4)$$

where ε_r is the rotational energy, ϕ the angle between the axis of rotation and the direction of the field, k is Boltzmann's constant 1.37×10^{-16} ergs/degree, and T is the absolute temperature.§

* The *time-averaged* moment $\bar{\mu}$ must be distinguished from the induced moment μ_i; actually, for the rigid dumb-bell model we are considering, μ_i is zero.

† Mensing and Pauli, *Physikal. Z.*, **27**, 509, 1926.

‡ Kronig, *Proc. Nat. Acad. Sci.*, **12**, 488, 1926.

§ Kallmann and Reiche, *Z. Physik*, **6**, 352, 1921; see particularly Fraser, *Molecular Rays*, p. 156 ff.

An idea of the order of magnitude of $\bar{\mu}$ is got by inserting typical numerical values in (4.4). Thus with $\mu_\epsilon = 10^{-18}$ E.S.U., E = 500 E.S.U., T = 300° K, we have $\bar{\mu} \sim 3 \times 10^{-3}\mu_\epsilon$.

Considering next the deflection suffered by a beam of dumb-bell molecules in an inhomogeneous electric field, we find, in close analogy to the magnetic case, that the deflection s of a single molecule at the exit of the field is given by

$$s = \tfrac{1}{4}.\bar{\mu}.(\partial E/\partial s)(l^2/\varepsilon_v) . \quad . \quad . \quad (4.5)$$

where $\partial E/\partial s$ is the inhomogeneity of the field (for example near a charged wire, or at the mouth of a parallel plate condenser), l the length of path in the field, and ε_v is the energy of translation corresponding to the single velocity v. Inserting numerical values ($\bar{\mu} = 3 \times 10^{-21}$ E.S.U., $\partial E/\partial s = 10^4$ E.S.U./cm., $l = 10$ cm., $\varepsilon_v = 10^{-13}$ ergs) we find $s = 7.5 \times 10^{-2}$ mm. Thus the deflections to be expected are small, in accordance with the fact that we are dealing here with a second order effect.

Equation (4.5) refers to the deflection of a single molecule, for which $\bar{\mu}$ and ε_v are both defined. In an actual molecular beam, however, ε_v can take all possible values subject to the Maxwell distribution law, and $\bar{\mu}$ all values defined by equations (4.3) or (4.4).

Consider the case of high temperature (4.4) first, for which a general treatment can be given. Inserting the values of $\bar{\mu}$ from (4.4) in (4.5) we have

$$\left.\begin{array}{l} s = C.\dfrac{3\cos^2\phi - 1}{\varepsilon_v.\varepsilon_r} \\[2mm] C = (\mu_\epsilon{}^2/16).E.(\partial E/\partial s).l^2 \end{array}\right\} \quad . \quad . \quad (4.6)$$

where ε_v, ε_r are both governed by a Maxwell distribution law; while all values of ϕ are equally probable, since the beam is collision free. For convenience, we set $s = \sigma.s_0$, where $s_0 = 2C/(kT)^2$ is the deflection suffered by a molecule for which $\varepsilon_v = \varepsilon_r = kT$ and $\phi = 0$; and obtain the probability $P(\sigma)d\sigma$ for the occurrence of deflections lying between σ and $\sigma + d\sigma$ by integration over the individual probabilities $P(\varepsilon_v)d\varepsilon_v$, $P(\varepsilon_r)d\varepsilon_r$, and $P(\phi)d\phi$.* Fig. 21 shows the resulting plot of $P(\sigma)$ against σ.

In the case of low temperature, where a classical continuum of rotation states cannot be assumed, there is only one continuously variable quantity, namely ε_v. Hence the probability $P_{J,M}(\sigma)d\sigma$ for the occurrence of deflections between $\sigma_{J,M}$ and $\sigma_{J,M} + d\sigma$ must be calculated for each state (J,M) and a summation curve constructed, each state being given its proper weight in accordance with a Boltzmann law.† An example of such a curve, for the case of HCl at 120° K, is seen in fig. 22.

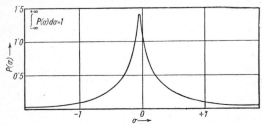

FIG. 21.—Calculated Intensity Distribution in an electrically deflected Beam (Case of Linear Rotator, High Temperature)

The salient feature of the deflection patterns to be expected, both at high and low temperatures of the source, is the absence of any splitting of the beam. In other words, the intensity distribution in the beam after passage through the field is in all cases *continuous*. The next thing to notice is that the maximum of the deflection pattern lies very close to the position of the undeflected beam. This is partly due to the fact that in adopting a rigid dumbbell model as the basis of calculation, the contribution of the polarizability to the deflection pattern has been neglected. In reality, the whole deflection pattern should be thought of as arising, not from a parent beam at $\sigma = 0$,

* See Fraser, *Molecular Rays*, p. 162 ff., also Scheffers, *Physikal. Z.*, **35**, 425, 1934.
† cf. Estermann and Fraser, *J. Chem. Phys.*, **1**, 390, 1933.

but from a beam deflected in the direction of the field by an amount depending on the polarizability α.* The effect is small, however, and may readily be approximated to, if not in many cases actually neglected in practice.

Thus we can say in general that the effect observed in an electric deflection experiment is a diminution of intensity at the position of the undeflected trace, coupled with

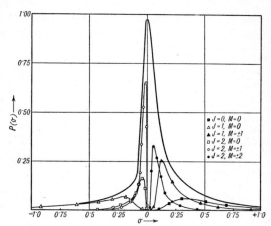

FIG. 22.—Calculated Intensity Distribution in an electrically deflected Beam of HCl at 120° K (Linear Rotator, Low Temperature)

a broadening of the beam, rather than a lateral deviation of the beam as a whole. This is in one sense a fortunate circumstance, for it is always possible to discover the value of the dipole moment μ_e merely from observation of the intensity diminution I/I_o at $\sigma = 0$, provided the form of the deflection pattern is known.† It is just here that the necessity for a metrical detector arises.

The first experiments in this direction were made by

---

* See Estermann and Fraser, loc. cit., p. 394 ; also Scheffers, loc. cit., p. 432.

† Estermann and Fraser, loc. cit., p. 398.

Estermann and Fraser (loc. cit.) on the type molecule HCl. The dipole moment and polarizability of this substance had already been measured accurately by the dielectric constant method,* and the interest of the beam experiments lies therefore mainly in the methodics. The detector used was the hot-wire manometer, which, since HCl is readily condensed and strongly adsorbed at the

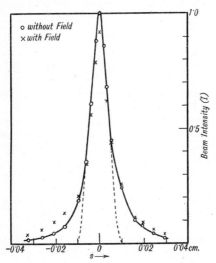

Fig. 23.—Observed Intensity Distribution in a Beam of HCl at Room Temperature, with and without Field (Estermann and Fraser)

walls of the gauge, could not be cooled below room temperature. The measurements were therefore troublesome, the comparatively small dipole moment of HCl adding to the difficulty of using the gauge under rather poor conditions of sensitivity. These points are illustrated in fig. 23, which shows an intensity plot both with and without field.

* Zahn, *Phys. Rev.*, **24**, 400, 1924.

TABLE VII

Substance :	Na I	K Cl	K Br	K I	Cs I	
Scheffers :	4·9	6·3	—	6·8	—	: μ_ϵ
Rodebush, Murray, and Bixler :	—	8·0	9·06	9·24	10·2	

Quantitatively, these measurements were of little value, but the experiments gave an opportunity to work out the procedure of evaluation ; * and more recently Scheffers (loc. cit.) and Rodebush, Murray, and Bixler † have obtained quantitative results with the more polar alkali metal halides, using the extremely sensitive surface ionization gauge as detector. Their results are set out for comparison in Table VII. The μ_ϵ values are expressed in Debye units ; those of Rodebush, Murray, and Bixler are as revised by Fraser and Hughes (loc. cit.). It will be noticed that there are considerable discrepancies in the two cases where the observations overlap, namely KCl and KI ; however, when all sources of uncertainty are taken into account, it seems likely that the differences are covered by a probable experimental error.

The Symmetrical Top. The type molecule is CH_3Cl. It is clear, alike on grounds of symmetry and from observation of infra-red spectra, that the direction of the molecular dipole moment, which is compounded of the group moments C—Cl,3(C—H), lies in the figure axis of the molecule (fig. 24A). The molecular model, the symmetrical top,‡ may be represented as a dumb-bell carrying a

* See also Fraser and Hughes, *J. Chem. Physics*, **4**, 730, 1936.
† Rodebush, Murray, and Bixler, *J. Chem. Phys.*, **4**, 372, 1936 ; see also Rodebush, ibid., p. 536.
‡ cf. Joos, *Theoretical Physics*. Blackie, 1934, p. 145 ff.

heavy disc at one end; it has three principal axes of rotation A, B, and C, with three corresponding moments of inertia $I_A = I_B \neq I_C$ (fig. 24B). Such a model is gyroscopic: that is, a collision with another molecule will give rise to a pure spin about the C axis, together with the precession of that axis about the direction of the total angular momentum J. If the molecule enters an electric field, the J-axis precesses in turn about the field direction.

Thus we should expect a symmetrical top molecule to

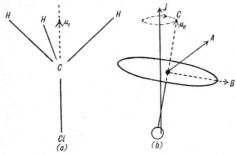

FIG. 24.—Illustrating Temperature Rotation of CH_3Cl (Symmetrical Top $I_A = I_B \neq I_C$)

possess a time-averaged moment $\bar{\mu}$ *to the first order*, since in general μ_e will have a component in the J-direction, in contradistinction to the dumb-bell model, for which μ_e is always at right angles to J.

Manneback * has obtained an expression for $\bar{\mu}$ in terms of the three quantum numbers J, M, and N, where $-J \rightleftharpoons \dfrac{M}{N} \rightleftharpoons J$. J is the total quantum number, defining the total rotational energy of the molecule, M refers to the motion of precession about the J-direction, and N to

* Manneback, *Physikal. Z.*, **28**, 72, 1929.

spin of the molecule about the figure axis. For any state (J, M, N)

$$\left.\begin{array}{l} \bar{\mu} = \mu_\epsilon . \dfrac{M.N}{J(J+1)} - \dfrac{8\pi^2 . I_A . \mu_\epsilon{}^2 . E}{h^2} \left(\phi_{J, M, N} - \phi_{(J+1), M, N} \right) \\[2mm] \phi_{J, M, N} = \dfrac{(J^2 - M^2)(J^2 - N^2)}{(2J-1).J^3.(2J+1)} \end{array}\right\} \quad (4.7)$$

or $\qquad \bar{\mu} = \frac{1}{3}.8\pi^2 . \mu_\epsilon{}^2 . I_A E / h^2$ if $J = M = N = 0$. $(4.7')$

Thus the lowest energy state contributes always a second order term only in μ_ϵ (compare equations $(4.7')$ and (4.3)); whereas all other states yield a first order term. Mr. J. V. Hughes * has carried through the rather heavy computation of $\bar{\mu}$ for methyl iodide, and finds that except at extremely high field strengths and low temperature, the second order term in (4.7) is only some hundredths of the first order term. In practice, therefore, only the first order terms need be taken into account.

The corresponding deflection pattern, while of the same general form as the linear rotator curves of figs. 21 and 22, is on a vastly different scale : $s \sim 1$ cm., as against 10^{-2} mm. for the linear rotator (cf. p. 58) ; moreover, I/I_0 at $\sigma = 0$ is 0·1 rather than 0·9. One may therefore anticipate the accurate determination of the dipole moments of symmetrical top molecules by the beam method.

There is, for example, the question of the structure of the free radical CH_3, for which a plane configuration $(\mu_\epsilon = 0)$ has been predicted.† Since μ (C—H) is of the order 0·4 Debye, it is clear that the angle between the C—H bonds and the figure axis has to depart by less than half a degree from the predicted right angle for a moment detectable by the beam method to result.

The Asymmetrical Top. The theory for molecules with a lower symmetry than the symmetrical top ($I_A \neq I_B \neq I_C$) is almost impossible to handle ; and we have seen that the evaluation of the dipole moment from a deflection pattern requires a previous knowledge of the shape of the

---

* Unpublished.

† Penney, *Trans. Faraday Soc.,* **31,***734, 1935.

ntensity distribution.   Hence no quantitative approach to
he study of the electrical nature of asymmetrical top
nolecules by the beam method is practicable.

ATOMIC POLARIZABILITIES

Owing to the very complete symmetry of their electrical
structures, atoms have uniformly zero dipole moment.

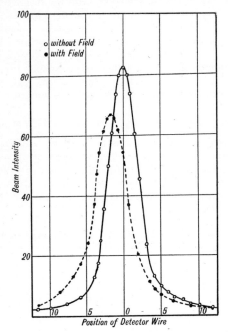

FIG. 25.—Polarizability of Potassium Atoms, measured by the
Deflection Method (Scheffers and Stark)

On the other hand, every atom is more or less deformable
electrically ; and measurement of atomic polarizabilities
may be expected to give useful information about inter-
atomic forces.

Measurements of the polarizability of alkali metal atom and of atomic hydrogen have been made by Scheffers and Stark.* Here the deflection pattern is extremely simple and directly interpretable. It consists of a single deflected beam, displaced in the direction of increasing electrical inhomogeneity, the amount of the deflection being proportional to the field strength. $\mu_i = \alpha.E$ is determined by measuring s_α, in close analogy with the magnetic deflection curves dealt with in the preceding chapter.

An example of the results obtained by Scheffers and Stark is shown in fig. 25. The potassium beam is received at a surface ionization gauge, and s_α is determined from measurement of s_m, the deflection corresponding to the maximum of the deflected beam (cf. p. 35). Similar results were obtained with lithium and caesium, thus :

	Li	K	Cs
α :	1·2	3·4	$4·2 \times 10^{-23}$ cm³.

The atomic hydrogen was received on a WO_3 target and α was determined by measurement of s_1 and s_2 in the deflected trace (cf. p. 36). The value of α obtained $(3 \pm 1).10^{-25}$ cm.³, is therefore much less accurate than those obtained with the alkali metals, where a metrical detector was used.

* Scheffers and Stark, *Physikal. Z.*, **35**, 625, 1934 (Alkali Metals) ; ibid., **37**, 217, 1936 (Hydrogen).

AUTHOR INDEX

SUBJECT INDEX

Printed in Great Britain by Butler & Tanner Ltd., Frome and London